# Knowledge in Mental Health: Reclaiming the Social

# APPLIED SOCIAL STUDIES – RECENT DEVELOPMENTS, INTERNATIONAL AND COMPARATIVE PERSPECTIVES (SERIES)

***Frank Columbus/Peter Herrmann***
***SERIES EDITORS***

## EDITORIAL BOARD

# KNOWLEDGE IN MENTAL HEALTH: RECLAIMING THE SOCIAL

LYDIA SAPOUNA
AND
PETER HERRMANN
EDITORS



**Nova Science Publishers, Inc.**
*New York*

For permission to use material from this book please contact us:
Telephone 631-231-7269; Fax 631-231-8175
Web Site: http://www.novapublishers.com



**LIBRARY OF CONGRESS CATALOGING-IN-PUBLICATION DATA**

Knowledge in mental health : reclaiming the social / Lydia Sapouna and Peter Herrmann (editors).
p. cm.
Includes index.
ISBN 1-59454-812-9
1. Mental health services--Europe. 2. Mental health policy--Europe. I. Sapouna, Lydia. II. Herrmann, Peter.
RA790.E9K56 2006
362.1--dc22 2005029400

*Published by Nova Science Publishers, Inc. ✣ New York*

*Dedicated to the memory of Kieran Crowe who fought for a social recovery agenda in mental health*

# CONTENTS

# ACKNOWLEDGEMENTS

This publication has been supported by the Research Publication Fund of the Faculty of Arts, University College Cork, Ireland. We thank Sally-Ann Attale for her skilful language editing of the contributions.

In: Knowledge in Mental Health
Editors: L.Sapouna and P. Herrmann, pp. 1-24
ISBN 1-59454-812-9


***Chapter 1***

# POLICY, PRACTICE AND RESEARCH AS KNOWLEDGE IN MENTAL HEALTH

***Lydia Sapouna[1] and Peter Herrmann[2]***
[1]Department of Applied Social Studies University College Cork, Ireland.
[2]The Independent Research Institute European Social Organisational Science Consultancy; Aghabullogue, Co. Cork,
The Department of Applied Social Studies University College Cork, Ireland

## PROLEGOMENA

"But I don't want to go among mad people," Alice remarked.
"Oh, you can't help that," said the Cat: "we're all mad here. I'm mad. You're mad."
"How do you know I'm mad?" said Alice.
"You must be," said the Cat, "or you wouldn't have come here."
*(From Alice in Woderland)*

## BACKGROUND

This book originates in the work of a Socrates European partnership on mental health promotion. The project involved partners from four European countries (the United Kingdom, Italy, Portugal and Ireland) and led to the development of a European Module on mental health promotion in each country, teaching exchanges and a series of conferences in the UK (2001), Ireland (2002) and Italy (2003). However, this book moves beyond the publication of conference proceedings to provide a broader debate on responses to mental distress that promote inclusion, citizenship (as expression of meaningful participation in the community) and a genuine alternative to institutional thinking and practices.

The title, *Knowledge in Mental Health – Reclaiming the Social,* indicates the areas of interest to the editors and contributors. A theme that consistently emerged in the course of the European partnership was the necessity to question existing knowledge in mental health as it pertains to politics, policy making, practice applications, research methodologies, and service evaluation. As a result, we identified the need to examine further the construction of such knowledge and find ways to challenge it at various levels (political, conceptual, policy, practice, research and evaluation methodologies). This means that acting in the field is analytically and practically embedded into the socio-philosophical frame in a meaningful way. In social science, we rarely find an issue where the link between the different aggregative levels is so close. In other words, it is in the area of mental health where the actual interaction and politically enforced separation and contradiction between the macro-, the meso- and the micro-levels are so closely tied. This makes it necessary to aim at grasping simultaneously the different areas. For this, we suggest as a rough guide concretising – and thus operationalising – the aggregative levels in the following way:

- The macro-level concerns both the political will of structuring the mental health sector and the legal and institutional frameworks underpinning mental health care. However, this has to be seen not simply as an expression of political ideologies of representatives of political parties, but as a manifestation of the «material forces» which establish certain patterns and mechanisms of gradual exclusion and inclusion. We will later show how this is closely linked to *(a)* the definition of citizenship and *(b)* consequently the dissociation of the public and the private. Subsequently, on this level the «published opinion» has to be considered, as has the attitude of society at large.
- The meso-level can be taken as the institutional system by which the exclusion actually takes place. Namely, we are concerned with the institutionalised system of health care in general and mental health care in particular. In this case institutionalisation is taken in the widest sense, including forms of «deinstitutionalised institutionalisation» *(as explored by Lydia Sapouna in her contribution on pages 85 ff.).* We are also concerned with the mechanisms of actually implementing legal regulations and «putting meat onto the bones» of formal structures through the development of new approaches to practice *(as explored by Kieran Crowe and Karen Taylor in their contribution on pages 25 ff.).*
- Finally, the micro-level is concerned with the individual actors, particularly in the field of mental health care (professionals in the medical and administrative field, relatives and communities concerned, and last but not least patients[1] with their different status).

Acknowledging the breadth of this task, this book aims to provide a framework wherein these levels of knowledge-making and their perpetuation will be discussed by focusing on two central discourses (types of knowledge) in current social policy and welfare, namely *risk management* and *evidence-based practice (EBP).*

Both the systemic implications concerned with the politics and policies and also the practice implications of the current emphasis on *risk* regulation and elimination in health and social care will be explored. The impact of definitions of risk and the prevailing «culture of

[1] The term «patients» is frequently used in this introductory text as we refer to the status that is attributed according to the «official view» and the mainstream psychiatric services. Rather than suggesting service users, we in general want to orient on the use simply of the term citizens.

safety» in responding to mental distress will be considered, and the risks posed to service users by psychiatric services will be discussed. Risk-taking will be contemplated as integral to autonomy, both as a matter of quality of life and social quality. Consequently it will be considered a founding block of actual citizenship.

Furthermore, the growing popularity of evidence-based practice in health and welfare contexts will be considered. Evidence-based practice has become an

> attractive remedy to the multiple pressures affecting contemporary health and welfare practice... and a means to ensure equity and best value. (Taylor/Whyte 2000: 5).

A search for certainty and consistency has led to another way of knowing based on factual information, rigorous procedures and measurable outcomes. However, it has also led to the development of technical/procedural approaches with limited questioning of how knowledge is made, produced or constructed by professionals themselves *(see ibid)*. Such approaches also fail to respond to the complexities and ambiguities that professionals encounter in their everyday practice. This trend will be discussed with particular emphasis on mental health service evaluation. The development of a hierarchy where certain types of (scientific) evidence are valued more than other types of evidence (such as service users' experiences) will be critically examined.

## Construction and Application of Knowledge in Mental Health – Guards in Prison

Challenging the prevailing forms of knowledge that historically informed mental health care is by no means a new trend. Changes in mental health services are closely linked with questioning the ways in which mental distress has been understood and dealt with throughout the years. Examples of such questions include the challenges posed to the dominance of biomedical approaches in defining and treating mental «illness» *(see Foucault, 1976; Scheff, 1966; Scull, 1975; Szasz, 1970, 1974)*, the analysis of the disastrous impact of institutional care *(see Barton, 1959; Basaglia, 1968; Foucault, 1967; Goffman 1961)*, and an extensive debate on the power of psychiatry *(see Miller Rose, 1986; Barker/Stevenson 2000)*. Further questions addressed the broader socio-political dimensions of psychiatric policy and practice and considered the position of people with mental health problems within the inequalities of the capitalist system *(see Rogers & Pilgrim 2003; Pilgrim & Rogers 1999; Scull, 1981)*.

Indeed, community mental health care is based, to a certain extent, on such ideological and theoretical developments. The danger is however that, in a period where community care is heralded as a «mainstream» policy rather than a «radical» approach to psychiatry, such analyses may appear rather dated. We argue that this is not the case. For example, four decades after *Goffman's* original analysis of the institutional syndrome, the question of institutionalisation is still very relevant as it can be traced in mental health policy, professional thinking and practice. However, in contemporary service provision the expression of institutional patterns of exclusion is far more subtle, and this is why we need to develop the tools to question constantly the nature of knowledge informing mental health theory and practice.

The authors will highlight the fact that despite the rhetoric of empowerment in mental health service provision and the development of community-based care, people with mental health problems continue to experience high levels of exclusion in social and community life. In order to provide meaningful alternatives to such exclusion, this book considers the construction and application of knowledge in the area of mental health as part of constructing citizenship. The multiple levels of relevance are recognised by making reference to political and contextual issues, policy-making, institutional and community-based practices, research methodologies and service evaluation.

The common thread linking the different aspects of the discussion is a consideration of risk management and evidence-based practice as specific modes of knowledge and knowing affecting mental health policy and practice. However, this is not meant to be solely a concern with specific methodologies and methods. Rather, we will show in the introduction that these are basically specific reflections of wider attempts at further «privatising the social».

## Risk Management and Welfare Provisions

### The Context

Risk assessment and management have become central components in social policy and social care practice. *Parton (1996)* argues that risk is a way of thinking rather than just a set of objective realities. It is a reflection of the changing ways in which social professionals view their practice. Such changes reflect a broader political climate, where citizenship is conceptualised as active citizenship and a strong emphasis is placed on personal fulfilment, individual choice and responsibility. At the same time, economic and social life is characterised by a whole variety of insecurities, uncertainties and fears, part of it making *Ulrich Beck* speak of a risk society *(see Beck 1992)*. These uncertainties and fears stand behind the fact that postmodernism is in vogue. However, risk in the way we are dealing with it is going much further than risks as unfathomable dangers that cannot be accounted to definite structures of human action and agency.

The risk *Beck* is talking about is forcing the individual into overwhelming structures he or she cannot control. The actual challenge for dealing with mental health issues in this context is the specific social pattern by which socially defined and «made» risks are redefined by politics as «dangerous situations» with which the individual has to cope. In other words, we find a process of individualising social concerns and increasingly closing the public realm – a general pattern, prevalent in social life and gaining specific relevance for «professionals» and service users alike in the (mental) health care system. In other words, we have to be critical of the way in which Beck uses the term and concept of risk as «neutral», as «something» the individual faces without hope of being able to change or even influence the situation. According to this view, «risk»is forcing the individual into overwhelming structures s/he cannot control; or more correctly is not supposed to control. In a climate where surviving uncertainties has become a major struggle, health and welfare professionals seek to find ways of coping with the uncertain and the unpredictable. Making reference to social work, *Parton* argues that the growing concerns about risk

> can be understood as both reflecting these increased anxieties, uncertainties and insecurities and as providing a rationale for coping, understanding and responding to the new situation. (Parton 1996: 99).

Risk can be seen therefore as a framework of understanding which affects directly the formation of professional practice. It has been argued that such frameworks keep health and welfare professionals tightly attached to models of practice by focusing on individual pathology and social control rather than social change *(see Kemshall 2002, Parton 1996/1998, Tanner 1998).* In other words, in such frameworks, social care practice loses its potential to explore the breadth of people's experiences and becomes increasingly de-politicised. These trends are reflected in the modes of knowledge informing social care and the types of questions with which social professions engage.

However, in order to explore this in greater depth we need to qualify further the term and concept of risk. For this, we start by differentiating between four types of risk within the mainstream definition:

a) acute and real (or as real perceived) «danger» for the immediate individual being – material threat, threat of fatal illness and similar eventualities can be mentioned, as well as, for instance, shock resulting from a car accident or other «external hazardous experiences».
b) following *Beck's* dictum, risk in the meaning of danger and as such showing two patterns:[2]
    1) The first is the dangers caused by precariousness in the widest sense, meaning the confrontation of the individual with the various decisions he or she has to face in the very specific social situation he or she is in. This is concerned with the fundamental class situation, requiring decisions on how life, i.e. reproduction, can be secured, what kind of risks will be taken in «balancing» for instance security of income on the one hand and acceptable working conditions (in terms of occupational safety and health, stress etc.) on the other hand. It may also be concerned with more specific «roles», as for example the role of mothers *(as mentioned in this text on page 11)* and also of fathers, for whom the typical role model remains that of the breadwinner – a role that is not (fully) compatible with the role of being a father.
    2) The second is the very «personal» risk-taking, the question of how an individual designs and shapes life on the very personal level, as despite social dependencies and embeddedness there is still discretion for personal decisions. There is risk-taking involved in nearly every decision, as far as *«Verstehen»,* i.e. understanding of a situation in *Weberian* terms is concerned.
c) risk in the understanding proposed by *Beck,* suggesting a universal «danger», which however is caused by human activities and action.

[2] Though *Beck* does not develop this differentiation.

## The «Social» as Space for Individual Development and Framework for Defining Risk

Such a differentiation allows us, however, to define also a common thread running through the different types of risk. First and foremost, risk can only be understood as relational matter. In other words, risk arises from the individual relating him/herself to others, be it other individuals, groups or institutional realities. As such, risk is something which comes close to social facts in the *Durkheimian* sense. Accepting this is hugely consequential with regard to mental health, i.e. the «definitions» and «treatments» of mental illness, be they professional or not, be they a matter of individual or social interpretation.

In particular, anthropology makes the general assumption that it is part of human nature to depend on «external guidance», as our own internal mechanisms of control are insufficient and in fact no longer exist, as the human being is characterised as a *«Mängelwesen»,* i.e. a creature that lacks guidance by instincts, looking for any sort of leadership and «cultural chains» in compensation for such a lack.[3] However, although we can readily agree with the statement that there is a need for feeling and being secure, the fundamental unpredictability and insecurity arises from external pressures and the fact that the means of control are systematically withheld. In other words, problems systematically arise where the individual is not allowed – due to the lack of material means or on the grounds of «moral control» – to control his or her own life according to standards other than those of the hegemonic ideology. Taking up general and fundamental critiques directed, for example, against *Hartmann, Scheler,* and later *Gehlen's* anthropological assumptions, the problem with such an approach is that it denies the actual fact that such a search for «stability» by the individual is very much an imposed one. As such, it contradicts the enlightened perspective from which *Immanuel Kant* writes of

> man's leaving behind its self-imposed immaturity. Immaturity

(and we could say instead the endless and clinging search for any kind of security)

> is the inability to employ one's own intelligence without being directed by someone else. The immaturity is self-imposed if it results not from a lack of intellect but from a lack of willingness and courage to use it without another's guidance. Supere Aude! (Kant, 1783: 53)

Such an approach denies, however, the individual's ability to manage reality independently. Nevertheless, if we follow the enlightened perspective, we are required to look at citizens rather than patients and service users respectively. This then means that in order to look at the space, the individual has to define him/herself in a socio-historical context. The challenge, then, is that such a condition does not only mean that risk is a relational matter, but moreover it is fundamentally a matter where the question always has to be asked for whom the actual risk arises. In this perspective, the «human being, lacking the guidance by instincts», the *«Mängelwesen Mensch»* is nothing else than the personality deprived of the right to be respected by society as an individual character. He or she is denied the right to

[3] This being very much the terminology *Arnold Gehlen (1942)* used.

manifest his/her own needs and wants towards society and in personal life. In other words, the problem is that there is a fundamental tension

- between stability and change and also
- between smooth evolution and concentrated disruption.

Of course, between each of these two poles lies a vast range of possible combinations.

Taking this together with the four different dimensions of risk as outlined before on *page 5*, we can see that the risk actually exists not solely – and primarily – as a pattern in which the individual is caught. Taking the definitional approaches provided as acceptable, we point to a further presumption, namely the fact that there is no «non-social» space. It is a fundamental fact of human existence that any individual act is in one way or another defined by previous, current or anticipated future social embedding, relations and interactions. This is also true in cases where we initially seem to be concerned with personal and intimate activities.

To build meaningfully upon this presumption of the non-existence of a non-social space, it is necessary to focus briefly on the core elements of a definition of the social. Here, we suggest the social being an outcome of the interdependencies between the self-realisation of individuals and the formation of collective identities, based on the outcomes of these interactions.

Without going into detail of this highly complex contemplation of understanding the social *(see Beck, Wolfgang et altera 2001),*[4] we can go on to draw attention to the interaction of conditional and constitutional factors as determinants of social quality – both of which are shown in the following graphs.

The conditional factors are presented as follows:

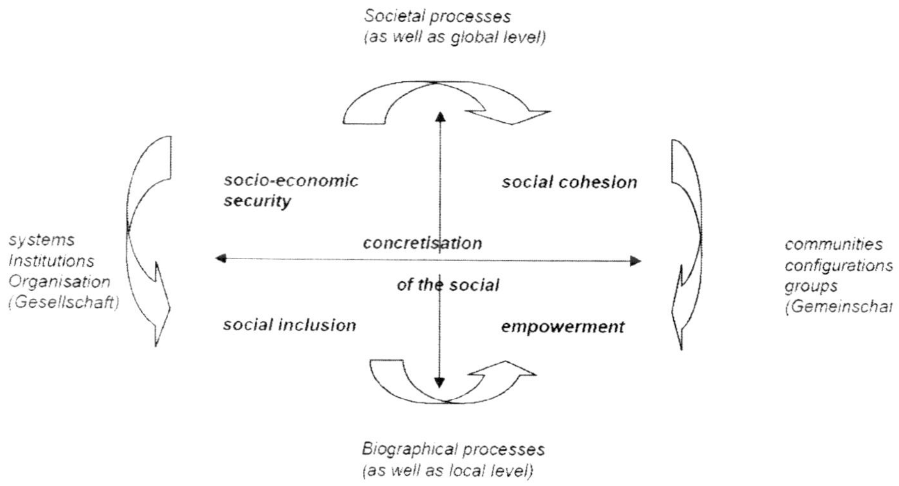


(van der Maesen et altera, 2004: 8)

[4] A further publication of the *European Foundation on Social Quality* is currently in preparation. Though due to be published end of 2005 a definite reference cannot yet be made.

Moving on to the constitutional factors, we see the following:

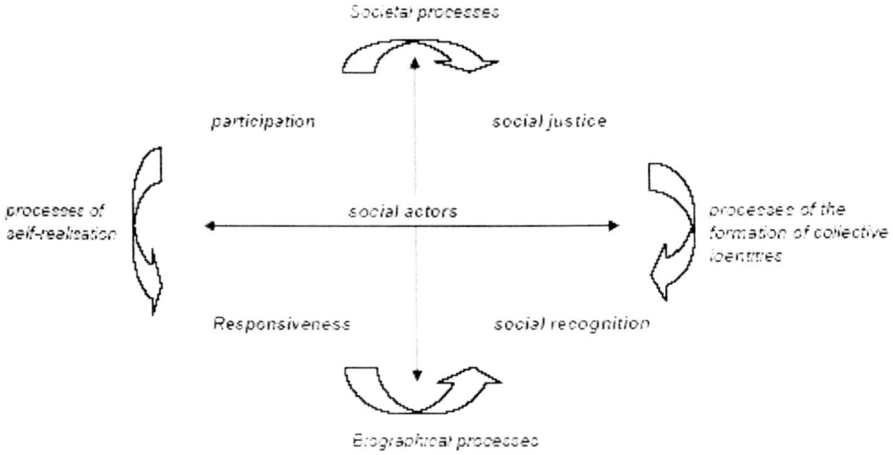


(ibid: 7)

Though there is already some relational outline involved in these arrangements – that provided by the relation within the set of conditional and constitutional factors – it is still an open and exciting question to explore the relationship between the two different sets. In a tentative proposal, one of the authors of this introduction outlined this in the form of a circle of mutually reinforcing (or complicating) relationships where, despite the overall dialectic relationship, at least some direct linkages between certain conditional and constitutional factors can be defined. This is presented in the graph below.

What is crucial for our context is the fact that by this approach we can overcome the dichotomisation of individual and social, as it is predominant in social science basically since its beginning. This does not suggest that there is a harmonious relationship between both; rather it points to power relationships and their actual constitution by the interaction of social actors on the grounds of their objective position in society, whether material or not. Furthermore, it allows us to emphasise the relational character by and in which individuals are defined and define themselves.

Coming back to the core of our topic, we can actually define risk on a scale as follows, providing again four dimensions. This links back to what has been already said with regard to the very general definition of risk *(see page 5),* namely

- risk for the personal identity;
- risk for the personal capacity to relate to other individuals;
- risk for the personal capacity to relate to «society» at large and its institutions;
- risk for society by the «demands» put forward by the individual.

In fact, we can locate the different risks in relation to the different conditional and constitutional factors, so that we arrive at the following matrix, which in this form at the same time suggests some kind of hierarchy.

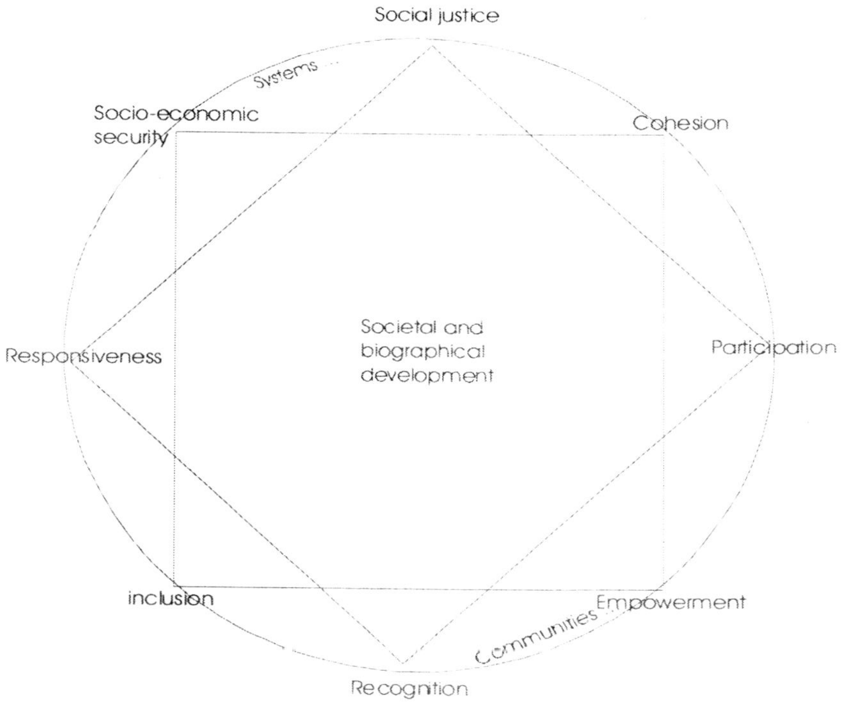


| Socio-economic security | Social inclusion | Social cohesion | Social empowerment |
|---|---|---|---|
| participation | responsiveness | social justice | social recognition |
| Risk for personal identity | risk for the personal capacity to relate to other individuals | risk for the personal capacity to relate to «society» at large and its institutions | risk for society by the «demands» put forward by the individual |

Returning to the dimensions of risk, it is in particular the last case, i.e. the «risk for society by the 'demands' put forward by the individual», which is of interest because of its complexity. First, it puts forward the question of whether the demands are actually «justified» or whether they are of such a kind that the individual actually overstretches «egocentric» attitudes and behaviour – all of this being very much historical and social constructs. In this sense they are closely linked to the prevailing structures of (re-)production in a given society.[5] Second, this is obviously closely linked to the question of power in the sense of the rights which an individual is granted «by society». From here, the immediate practical challenge is to overcome the term and concept of the patient and to refer instead to the term and concept of the citizen. Third, the «individual» in all these cases may well be an individual as an «isolated personality». However, even as such (s)he may also be – consciously or not – a member of a group that is stigmatised as «mad», as «mentally ill», simply because the individual is defined as a member of a group that is a threat to society's integrity. It is not difficult to find examples of this. Political terrorists, for instance in the case of members of the German RAF, the Irish IRA or religious fundamentalist movements are treated in this

[5] See in this context the redefinition and extension of regulationist approach in *Ryan/Herrmann 2004* and *Herrmann/Ryan forthcoming*

way. Having had their claims to be treated as political prisoners rejected, they are ordinarily criminalised and at the same time declared «mad». Fascism was characterised by frequently and intentionally identifying political resistance and criminal offences as mental illness. The German concentration camps were one of the most frightening examples of the consequences of such misuse of power in the name of «social integrity» as the highest good of the people *(«das Volksgut»)*. Less obvious, but no less dangerous, is the contemporary ongoing discrimination and degrading of ethnic minorities or of gays and lesbians. In actual fact, only up until recently it was the norm to talk about members of the travelling community and gay and lesbian people as people with «mental defects». In Ireland, for example, the term «social deviance», which included the «diagnosis of homosexuality», was only removed from the definition of mental illness with the publication of the *Mental Health Act* in 2001.

## Implications for Practice

Such patterns of thought and practice are particularly evident in the area of mental health.

> Risk avoidance and the 'worship' of safety are key features of mental health policy. The 'history of madness' has been characterized as a history of social regulation and normalization of the 'Other', in which segregation, surveillance and control of the mentally ill are central (Kemshall 2002: 98).

However, segregation and surveillance of the insane are not unique in the asylum era. Community care is also preoccupied with risk avoidance and risk management. While de-institutionalisation and community care aimed to promote the needs and rights of people with mental health problems, the current focus on risk avoidance and regulation in mental health policy, law and practice results in a negative view of user risks, and endangers the rights of an already vulnerable population. This argument is extensively explored by *Jim Campbell* in the chapter on pages 25 ff. In a discussion of service user rights, it is also important to highlight the contribution of the risk-taking approach. Risk taking has been developed by practitioners working towards service user involvement and empowerment. Its conceptual and value base considers risk taking as an integral part of a «normal», autonomous life and a condition of citizenship. It is also a way to challenge the oppressive and paternalistic practices of mental health professionals *(see Ramon, 1991; Braye and Preston Shoot, 1995; Davis, 1996; Kemshall, 2002)*. The overemphasis on risk-avoidance and the need to create space for calculated risk in mental health social work is elaborated by *Shulamit Ramon* on *pages 39 ff.*

It is at this point that we have to ask again for whom risk arises in practical terms. The emphasis of risk-avoidance applies anthropological approaches that have already been critically discussed *(s. page 6)* and which suggest that risk is fundamentally negative. However, it has been pointed out that it only makes sense to talk about risk if it is conceptualised in a relational understanding. In practical terms, then, risk is very much concerned with developing checks and balances, by which – on the basis of existing systems of power distribution – the various interests are defined, justified, rejected and finally implemented. This concern ranges from the aforementioned fundamental political questions (the definition of political enemies as «mad» and even «diabolic»), to more subtle issues such as repression and displacement of individuals by family members. In this sense, mental health institutions frequently function as a collecting tank for people for whom no other place – neither the family, nor a shelter for the homeless nor, a prison cell – is left. To be blunt, many of the cases of institutionalised mental health care are not much more than forms of deportation in cases where – to borrow a term used by *Rosa Luxemburg* – mechanisms of «inner colonialisation» fail to function. Society should be able to cope with difference by inclusion and integration. It should also be sufficiently open to divergence, allowing individuals to take non-standard decisions and develop their own life-styles. However, if such mechanisms and openness are not sufficiently in place, risk is being redefined. It is the individual who is seen as a risk for him/herself. In consequence, they are moved out of the way, seemingly justified by the need to «protect themselves».

The emphasis on risk avoidance in contemporary community care services has ultimately led to the construction of a two-tier system of mental health provision where «high risk individuals» are extensively managed in order to be securely contained, and «low risk cases» are rendered invisible. Indeed, within the current climate of welfare provision, availability of services is tightly linked with notions of risk and dangerousness. This is obvious in both the development of and access to services. Public funding is made more easily available to projects and initiatives targeting «populations at risk». Risk is a justification for service development and a vehicle to access support.

It is unhelpful simply to deny the usefulness of all such interventions. For example, the dramatic increase of male suicide is a major cause of concern in Ireland. Suicide is now the highest cause of death in young men aged 15-24 years *(see for instance SHB, 2002)*. Young men have been identified as a population «at risk» and targeting this group has been set as a priority by a number of initiatives, including the new Irish health promotion strategy *(Department of Health and Children, 2000)*.

This in itself can be seen as a positive preventative measure as there is now a framework for the recognition and protection of the needs of a potentially vulnerable group. However, problems occur when this process of recognition takes place out of context. Mentioning risk without mentioning the context in which the risks take place may lead to decontextualisation of risk and ultimately decontextualisation of life, as what really makes people suicidal or simply frightened is not being considered *(see Berke, 2003)*.

Furthermore, problems may occur when risk assessment as a new form of pathological categorisation becomes a primary criterion for eligibility. For example, there is no doubt that mothers who suffer from depression need support. However, if availability of services is directly linked with notions of risk and assessment of «inadequacies», problems will arise. *Tanner (1998)* talks about a new type of classification of deserving and undeserving, based on the degree of their perceived risk. If such a classification constitutes the main professional tool to relate to service users' experiences and needs, we need to seriously consider a number of implications.

In the case of maternal depression, we need to consider how the needs of these women are interpreted through professional interventions. Are they getting attention as people who, because of their mental health needs, are struggling with parenting? This does not seem to be the case. Maternal depression is recognised as a potential risk factor to the children involved and interventions are primarily concerned with the achievement of changes in mothering rather than the mother's mental health in its own right *(see White 1996)*. In other words, the mental health needs of women become invisible through this process.

Linking availability of services to assessment of «high risk» means that practitioners are obliged to emphasise risk rather strength when arguing for services for their clients. Such an approach dramatically reduces the scope for preventative intervention and promotion of well-being *(see Tanner, 1998)*. It also means that risk is frequently defined not only negatively but narrowly, as approaches to risk management tend to pathologise individuals *(see Kemshall 2002, Tanner 1998)*. Risk is located in factors

> intrinsic to them [individuals] or their immediate environment (Tanner 1998:19)

rather than the broader social context. This is manifested in the nature of assessment, primarily focusing on individual needs and risks attached to individual behaviour, such as risks in parenting, rather than risks arising from wider social economic or political factors which may make parenting difficult to manage.

Returning to the wider definition of risk, we can point to the following dimensions which are of immediate relevance for the practice.

a) It is a definition arising immediately from certain interests and
b) it has the (unspoken) aim of excluding people.
   Taking these two points, we have a more or less direct translation of «general political and social values», laid down in terms of a «good citizen» into a system of gradual institutional care for people defined as mentally ill. This is complemented and in a way based on mechanisms of subjective attributions, so that we can say that the incapability of society to cope with risk and difference is projected onto «the other» who are then blamed
c) directly or
d) indirectly by making him/her «feeling bad» about his/her feelings, ideas ....

This can be seen as completion of the hierarchical relationship of accumulation regimes, modes of regulations, life regimes and modes of life *(see footnote 4 in this chapter)*.

## Limits of Professionalisation

Looking more closely at the question of the professional systems of support and treatment, we find an interesting development which is usually faded out from the debate concerning professions, which are seemingly gaining independence from other forces. This development is the process by which professions are gaining independence and detachment, developing their own interest-rules, but doing so under certain conditions. Professions work within a certain system that is shaped by their own interests and also by the structure of social (re-)production. As such, professional ideas and values cannot be pure when led by any imagined «value-free idea of treatment and care». Embedded in the overall and very general processes of defining what is normal,[6] they are furthermore part of a system in which their services are provided. The understanding of rationality underlying these ideas and values is

[6] Which does not necessarily mean that they positively stick to the mainstream definition – but in a Christian society even the devil is defined with reference to god.

one of supposed technical neutrality – a typical example of Habermas' thesis of colonialisation. We can refer to the early formulation of *Habermas'* thesis as a point of reference, where he states in a brief essay

> As rationality of this kind refers to the correct choice between strategies, the appropriate application of technologies and suitable arrangement of systems (referring to *set* aims in *given* situations) it withdraws from any reflection and rational reconstruction of the societal interests under which the choice of strategies takes place, technologies are applied and systems are established. In addition, this rationality is only concerned with the relation of possible disposabilities and requires in consequence a type of action that implies ruling – be it ruling over nature or over society. Instrumentally rational action is in its very structure the execution of control. (Habermas, 1968: 49 – translation p.h., bold in original)

Such an analysis actually goes back much further and is not much more than an application of the *Marxian* perspective of the increasing

- commodification
- alienation, and finally
- fetishisation of commodities.

Applying the analysis to the question of professional assessments, we can say that what appears to be a matter of «professional performance» is actually very much the opposite, namely the ousting of professional principles from the professional world.[7] What has to be highlighted here is the fact that it is not the replacement of professionalism by other patterns of organisation or the replacement of one profession by another. Rather, we are dealing with matters of a redefinition of professional principles by principles «from outside». In particular, such a shift can be interpreted as a pattern of «privatisation», by which previously public control is taken back into a kind of private realm.

In terms of the organisational structure of service provision, one important aspect is the fact that the evolving pattern is very much one which takes the provision out of the public sphere. Whereas professional action had been originally very much shaped by «responsibility of the professional to the public», the protection of «patients» against private interests, and the development of a service system on the basis of demand,[8] we now find irregular patterns of care-systems led by principles of supply.[9] In short, professional reference is evidently the system of health care provision rather than the demand of «service users».

---

[7] A complex debate could be developed around this, as such process of ousting a specific rationality by another one reflects very much a fundamental problem of modernisation, which one of the authors of this introduction frequently pointed out *(e.g. Herrmann, 1998; and forthcoming)*

[8] It has to be mentioned that this is not to be seen as an absolute pattern

[9] By the way, this goes parallel with economic waves and as well with the dominant economic paradigms.

## Interim Conclusions: Liberating the Imprisoned Guards and Reintroducing the Public

Summarising and concluding so far, the institutionalisation of mental health care[10] and even more so the orientation on risk avoidance need to be spelled out as matter of privatisation and as a declaration of the societal and social status quo as invariable – unchanging and unchangeable. The risk of change and asking for change is the risk of the individual. If we refer more closely to questions on citizenship, a key problem with risk avoidance (and also with approaches to «evidence-based practice») is that these approaches reflect the supposedly superceded concept of passive citizenship. The key elements defining citizenship in the interpretation of T.H. Marshall, i.e. civil, political and social rights *(see Marshall, 1950)* are not principally withheld when it comes to people who are declared as mentally ill. However, they are «granted from above» and provided in a controlled, disintegrated way. As in the early phases of a traditional passive conceptualisation of citizenship

> *the king is all powerful and the subject is the recipient of privileges (Turner 1990: 207),*

the pattern repeats though the agencies change. With reference to our topic, adapting the previous quote, we can say that

> the professional is all powerful and the subject is the recipient of «allowed risks», being expected to adapt without any right to expect change in the conditions of the circumstances in which he or she lives.

The entire process of redefining citizenship and the professional relationship in the private realm – paradoxically taking place as a public process[11] – requires re-opening. Such a re-opening highlights the fact that citizenship, and consequently the right to take risks, is at stake. In other words, the demand for reopening logically requires community involvement as the only alternatively available «external force» that can counteract the dominant process of cocooning in a private sphere.

We can see that this framework is particularly damaging for the role of social professions in mental health, which could provide an alternative to the narrow view of medical assessment by utilising their potential to look at the social context of mental distress. This reflects the ambiguity of professionalisation, being on the one hand concerned with social control and development of knowledge, but on the other hand providing an «institutional framework of its privatisation» – in the sense of monopolised knowledge, controlled by and accessible for the professional only, not being open for challenges by others.

This, then, closely links into the «market framework» as an equally «semi-private» mechanism of control – a pattern that actually matches very much the reductionist approach of modernisation as a pattern underlying capitalist societies. Such a «lack of modernity» is partly due to a lack of divergences between productive forces and relations of production – or

[10] This taken in the widest sense

[11] As it is taking place as part of a general political process of privatisation and redefining citizenship

we can say a matter of contradictions between the different factors that have been previously outlined as factors of social quality *(s. page 7f.)*. This is basically what has been described in a specific context before as decontextualisation *(s. page 11)*. Conversely, thinking through such idealist approaches as *Kantian* understanding of enlightenment or *Humboldt's* humanism would substantially mean that this contradiction is overcome. This, of course, involves the *Marxian* understanding of turning idealism from its head onto the feet – as Marx rigorously did with *Hegel*. This leads us to the rejection of post-modernist suggestions of vagueness – in both scientific contemplation and every day's life.

We can apply here what *Antonio Gramsci* stated:

> Other ideologies are non-organic creations because they are contradictory, because they aim at reconciling opposed and contradictory interests; ... The philosophy of practice ... does not tend towards the peaceful resolution of the contradictions existing within history. It is itself the theory of those contradictions. (Gramsci, 1932-35: 196 f.)

Such recognition of contradictions as elementary forms of the private and public, as well as individual and social life, can only be reached if we also recognise a fundamental right to risk-taking.

From here we can equally say that interventions based on interpretations of «dangerousness» and «individual inadequacies» can be more destructive than constructive. For example in the case of maternal depression, an intervention may ultimately reinforce a sense of guilt and hopelessness in women who may feel penalised for experiencing mental distress, or who simply struggle with motherhood.

Taking a wider perspective, we also need to realise that interpreting and prioritising risk and need are actually a political activity. For example, referring frustrated parents to parenting courses instead of lobbying for better childcare facilities and community resources is a political act. Similarly, ignoring the way service users define risks and needs in their own lives also has political implications.

Finally, through this individual nature of assessment, other major risks are ignored. These are risks arising from the «treatment» or the intervention itself. For example,

> for mental health service users, the risk of causing harm to others is far less than the risks posed to them by their 'mental patient' status and treatment. (Tanner 1998:19)

Indeed, research on the experiences of mental health service users suggests that stigma, lack of information on diagnosis and treatment, mistreatment, over-emphasis on medication, inaccessibility of services, lack of community-based support, poverty and unemployment are often more damaging to the person that the illness itself *(see Rogers et al., 1993; SHB, 2002; Brosnan et al., 2002)*.

The actual methodological conflict between profession and service-providing institution is partly caused by the simultaneity of being a «social act». This is true even though we are dealing with an individual situation. The «alternating translation» between the social and individual levels of activity does not take place to a sufficient and adequate extent. In other words, the social and the individual alike are undialectically defined as «distinct» and even different, independent spheres.

## Defining Good Practice – Seeking Clarity

There is now a general agreement that social care practice is affected by an increase of legalistic and regulatory frameworks *(for a fuller discussion see Dominelli, 1996; Ferguson & O'Reilly, 2001; Preston-Shoot, 1998; Walsh, 1997)*. In the area of social work, such developments have led to the clarification of the professional role in certain areas by providing specific guidelines for practice. This trend has been welcome to a certain extent as it has provided a forum for the recognition of social problems such as child abuse, which have been silenced and neglected for too long.

Furthermore, clarity facilitates the development of professional confidence, the significance of which cannot be underestimated. However, problems arise if confidence is based primarily on the mastering of rules, regulations and assessment guidelines. *Howe (1992)* argues that a concern with risk assessment and the development of procedures to ensure that such assessments are properly carried out represent attempts to struggle with and make uniform a countless range of probabilities. Such attempts, though, simplify the complex elements of human interaction which the social professions deal with, and as a result they become de-skilled in looking at the broader picture of their clients' experience.

What kind of knowledge-base does this suggest for the social professions? The current preoccupation with performance-oriented practice is described by *Howe* as a shift from «depth» to «surface» in social work practice and thinking. A manifestation of this shift is that social workers now ask *what* clients do rather than *why* they do it.

> Behaviour is no longer analysed in an attempt to explain it. Rather it is assessed in terms of administrative procedures, political expectations and legal obligations. (Howe in Parton 1996: 88)

The same trend may lead to the emergence of what *Dominelli* describes as a "*discrete and fragmented vision of the social work task*" *(Dominelli, 1996:170)*. She links this trend with the development of a competency-based approach to social work. She argues that such an approach separates out various elements of complex social interactions and results in a fragmented, de-politicised practice. In this context, as *Preston-Shoot (1998)* succinctly argues, good practice is reduced to procedurally correct practice.

So are social professions losing the «social», in both practice and thinking? In the current practice in particular of what is called evidence-based practice, the understanding of the experience of mental distress is based on mastering technical knowledge and procedures. This entails the danger that we merely re-invent models of simplifying and regulating human pain – these models being in their underlying thinking very much the same as models of institutionalisation. A real change in thinking about the place that mental distress occupies in the social world cannot be based on simplifications. It has to be based on the validation of human history and the complexity of human life – interpreting individual history as the interpretation and implementation of social history. Therefore, it is very important for mental health professionals to provide a holistic rather than a fragmented understanding of the quality of people's experiences through research that moves far beyond technical frameworks of inquiry.

Thus, the necessity of reducing complexity cannot by itself be managed by translating reality into an «artificial» language of highly different and contested matters. In other words, what we commonly find is that issues of mental health are translated into a language that is driven by (micro-)economics, administration and by socio-political deprivation of the right of decision-making. However, what we need to do is to answer questions around mental distress in a language that develops arguments on the very same substantial level of individual and social history.

## WHAT CONSTITUTES EVIDENCE IN EVIDENCE-BASED PRACTICE?

In discussing the «making of knowledge» in mental health within such a technocratic culture, it is now important to consider further the growing popularity of evidence-based practice (EBP). This approach advocates that

> good practice is ultimately to be delivered by research informed evidence which is underpinned by rigorous and effective methodologies (Webb, 2001: 58),

and more broadly the application of scientific perspectives and models in practice. It also includes

> a concern with 'what works', and the application of interventions shown through research to be effective in changing behaviour. The tendency has been towards a narrow focus on behaviourist and regulatory approaches that target individuals, in the expectation that definitive tools and measurements will be identified in an attempt to measure change and productivity" (Humphries, 2003: 81f.).

One of the fundamental incentives to adopt such a framework is the market imperative, the belief that basing practice on such scientific methods can produce a more effective and economically accountable means of social service *(see Webb, 2001).* In other words,

> the achievement of the desired outcomes in the quickest possible time at the least possible cost (ibid: 86).

The application of this ideology within the current climate of severe cutbacks in the health sector endorses *Webb's* claim that evidence-based approaches are more likely to gain popularity in social organisations experiencing resource crises, human resource rationalisations even new restructuring strategies and increased monitoring of accountability *(see Webb, 2003).* The limitations of such developments go beyond the scope of this book. For the purpose of this discussion, however, we need to consider the impact of this technocratic culture on the development of ways of knowing in mental health research and practice.

An important question overlooked within this culture concerns both the nature and the making of knowledge. As *Taylor and White* argue, the

> problem with evidence-based practice and the production of outcome measures is that they are concerned exclusively with how knowledge is used, not how knowledge is made, produced or

> 'constructed' by professionals themselves. They do not allow access to the 'sense-making' processes of practitioners (Taylor/White, 2000: 5).

For example, they do not explore the many different ways in which a mental health problem can be explained or categorised. Furthermore, there is no recognition that the very diagnosis of «mental illness» is itself a social construct, a product of interaction rather than a mere application of neutral scientific knowledge. Knowledge in terms of «therapeutically-oriented» understanding is – as any everyday knowledge or scientific knowledge - always partial; a knowledge based on the analysis and normative assessment of social reality. In this sense, it always depends on three forms of biased interactions, namely

- the interaction during which both the «problem» and «illness» are made manifest
- the relationship through which knowledge is constructed and applied in a form of expert assessment, thus defining a situation as a «mental health problem»
- the dealings by which the problem and its «treatment» are defined – treatment referring to the entire range of formal and non-formal, «medical» and non-medical, socio-cultural, institutional, and other ways of dealing with the matter.

These three forms can be seen as classifications, as such covering the different specific forms that interactions can take. In the western world, psychiatry defines and treats «mental illness» within a biomedical framework, excluding other possible explanations of mental distress including social sources. Paradoxically, professions such as social work, by definition dealing with the «social» in mental health care, have a limited scope for working with people in their social situation. The social is basically reduced to an «individual relationship» rather than being regarded as a complex dialectic relationship as pointed out above.

A further question that is lost within such technical frameworks of knowledge is that of whose knowledge is valid. This is a pertinent question in the field of mental health, where historically the views and experiences of service users have been undermined because of their association with the «patient» status. An improvement of the mental health care system needs to address such long-established power imbalances. However, this is hard to achieve through approaches which emphasise the validity of scientific methodologies, as these serve to empower the practitioner more than the client *(Reid and Zettergen, 1999; Beresford and Croft, 2001; Humphries, 2003).*

While there is some evidence of service user involvement in mental health research, such involvement often implies the collection of research data with limited or no input in the analysis and publication of the findings *(see Speed, 2002).* In this model of participation, as *Beresford* and *Croft* argue,

> while the aim may be to make change, control still remains with the service system (Beresford/Croft, 2001: 296).

It has been argued that evidence-based approaches may undermine not only service user knowledge but also professional judgement and discretion. By providing limited and rather artificial frameworks for inquiry, they fail to capture the messiness of practice and the complex dilemmas confronted by welfare professionals *(Taylor/White, 2000; Humphries, 2003).* The current emphasis on technical ways of knowing, based on checklists and grades of evidence indicators to ensure reliability and validity of the research, discourage forms of interpretive inquiry that attempt to explore the complexities of service users' experiences. However, it is not just service user experiences that may be lost through the evidence-based model. The broader factors affecting professional decision-making and interventions, including agency politics, managerial priorities, community interests and cultural factors, are also ignored *(Webb, 2001)*.

## CONCLUSION

Thus, we can summarise under three headings the different perspectives and implementations elaborated in the individual contributions of the present volume.

Policy and practice issues examining:

- How conceptual and operative frameworks guiding mental health care tend to lead to further regulation and control, thus endangering the rights of an already vulnerable group. This argument is elaborated by Jim Campbell, Bill Healy and Lisa Brophy on pages 25 ff.
- The oppressive nature of risk avoidance in mental health care and the potential of calculated risk-taking for service user empowerment are shown by Shulamit Ramon on pages 39 ff.
- A paradigmatic shift in the understanding and treatment of mental distress. This includes a shift from 'incurable mental illness' and models of certainty and normality guiding treatment, to severe emotional distress from which people can recover. Recovery is contingent to an environment where people are facilitated to reconstruct what is important to them, in order to provide them with more options, choices and hope. The contribution by Kieran Crowe and Karen Taylor on pages 57 ff. gives evidence on this topic.

Institutional and contextual issues where:

- Caterina Corbascio-Fox on pages 69 ff. understands deinstitutionalisation as a process of re-acquiring social and civil rights, currently threatened by the direction of health politics.
- Institutionalisation is understood as a process of exclusion that goes beyond physical incarceration. Lydia Sapouna on pages 85 ff. considers institutionalisation to be a form of thinking and practising, with a distinct political character, which fails to take a broader view of mental distress. Despite the rhetoric of community care, institutionalisation remains prevalent in contemporary mental health policy and practice.

Research methodologies and service evaluation where:

- Shulamit Ramon on pages 101 ff. discusses service user-led research as a meaningful tool for service evaluation.

- Miguel Xavier on pages 119 ff. reconsiders evaluation models in order to produce models that provide a fuller understanding of the ways in which service users and their carers experience mental health services.

In the wider perspective of the introduction, which aims at bringing together the various perspectives on a more abstract level, it is interesting to note that evidence-based practice is actually not simply and primarily a method which can be found in mental health «care». Rather it is fundamentally a method characterising the development of politics. In very general terms it can be seen as a utilitarian shift in the debate on citizenship, as such being part of a general shift of contemporary societal developments, limiting at the one end what is being opened up at the other end. In other words, the marked shift from governing to governance, the growing openness towards «the citizen» and the increasing number of NGOs in the process of decision-making can be seen as the «open end». Incidentally, it is not surprising that this development finds its origin very much in the Anglo-Saxon world, being just one part of the implementation of the utilitarian «social-managerialist» politics. Apparently, ruling groups and classes – in political and professional circles – suggest a demeaning of their power position. Of course, this is a response to the growing mistrust in their performance – be it evoked by open scandals or be it an expression of an increasing enlightenment of broader groups of the population, made possible by the accessibility of information. However, there are always good reasons to be wary of any silent revolution – and so it is the case here. The enforced openness is answered by raising the forefinger, the request for «objective control». There are good reasons for developing safeguards to avoid one kind of misuse of power being replaced by a similar misuse of power by another group. However, as argued in the introduction, the contention that evidence-based practice is an alternative can only claim limited ... – well, limited evidence.

Thus, the main conclusions are as follows:

- Although we do not want to preach relativism, there is no absolute and moreover no neutral truth simply resulting from scientific research as suggested by the principles of evidence-based practice. Briefly, science is highly historically bound, coined by the productive relationship[12] and consequently not least embedded in power-relationships, which are particularly evident in the field of mental health care.
- Such a relational character of science means not least that this supposed neutrality is nothing more than the acceptance of one single rationale as eternal and unquestionable (e.g. a psychiatric diagnosis or treatment plan) – a political imperative, based on power-relationships, that creeps into all fibres of the social fabric. Such relationships have historically marginalised service users' voices by turning people into 'mental patients' and thus rendering them undeserving or incapable of holding full citizenship status.
- It follows that such an orientation on evidence-based practice is very much a matter of stabilising existing power structures. Contradicting in itself, though being a political – and therefore public – issue it paradoxically is based on the ideology of

[12] This is not to suggest a blunt mechanical pattern. Rather, this is a somewhat simplifying expression of the fact that science is very much a socialised activity – even ideas from geniuses as *Georg Simmel, Sigmund Freud* or *Albert Einstein,* who seemingly worked as isolated individuals had been minted to a large extent by the spirit of their time.

privatisation. Decisions are taken out of the soci(et)al context and discourse, shifted to private decisions.

- Consequently, risk taking is not accepted and therefore has to be eliminated. While there is a legitimate professional concern about the engagement with dangerous situations, the current political imperative of risk avoidance is leading to a utilitarian subordination to the principles of the given structures of consumption and administration.

  > The essence of the NPM [New Public Management] doctrine is a change in the culture of public service delivery and a deliberate attempt at the level of discourse to reconstitute the client, the patient or the claimant as a 'customer'. Under the subsequent New Labour government, though the overall managerialist language of NPM became less prominent, many of its essential objectives have been subsumed within the government's 'modernisation' agenda … . This included the introduction of Best Value reviews for all local government services and a technocratic emphasis of 'evidence based' policy and practice. (Dean 2002: 17)

- Finally, rights are externally defined and «granted» by the supposedly «neutral» evidence. This leads back to what has been said before, namely that there is no neutral scientific evidence, thus no neutral ground on which rights can justifiably be «granted from above». In other words, we arrive at the first point of these summarising points; we find a certain vicious circle in which evidence-based practice in actual fact reduces systematically the acknowledgement of rights in their own terms. There are:

  > Different ways in which welfare rights are ideologically constructed and … different ways in which the bearers of such rights are socially constituted. (ibid: XV)

Citizens have to stand up for their rights, and patients have to stand up for their right to be citizens. For this process to be meaningful, however, 'rights' cannot be externally defined or granted. They should be defined and developed by the accumulation of *evidence, based* on people's experience of distress in a social context. So, in this light it can be a very social and public undertaking to follow the seemingly individualist invitation of *Dante*

> Vien dietro a me, e lascia dir le genti:
> sta come torre ferma, che non crolla
> già mai la cima per soffiar de' venti;
> chè sempre l'uomo in cui pensier rampolla
> sovra pensier, da sé dilunga il segno
> perché la foga l'un dell'altro insolla.[13]
>
> (Dante: 68)

## References

Barker, P./Stevenson, C. (eds.), 2000: *The Construction of Power and Authority in Psychiatry*, Oxford: Butterworth-Heinemann.

Barton, R., 1959: *Institutional Neurosis*, Bristol: Wright.

Basaglia, F., 1968: *L'istituzione Negata*, Rome: Einaudi.

Beck, U., 1992: *The Risk Society*, London: Sage.

Beck, Wolfgang/van der Maesen, Laurent J.G./Walker, Alan, 2001: Theorizing Social Quality: The Concept's Validity; in: Beck, Wolfgang/van der Maesen, J.G. Laurent/Thomése, Fleur/Walker, Alan (Eds.): *Social Quality: A Vision for Europe*; The Hague/London/Boston: Kluwer Law International: 307 ff..

Beck, Wolfgang/van der Maesen, Laurent J.G./Walker, Alan, 2001: The Concept's Empirical and Political Applicability; in: Beck, Wolfgang/van der Maesen, J.G. Laurent/Thomése, Fleur/Walker, Alan (Eds.): *Social Quality: A Vision for Europe*; The Hague/London/Boston: Kluwer Law International: 361 ff..

Beresford, P./Croft, S., 2001: Service Users' Knowledge and the Construction of Social Work, in: *Journal of Social Work*, 1(3): 295-316..

Berke, J.H., 2003: The Right to be at Risk in: Critical Psychiatry Network Website, *http:/www.critpsynet.freeuk.com/Berke.htm.*

Braye, S./Preston-Shoot, M., 1995: *Empowering Practice in Social Care*, Buckingham: Open University Press.

Brosnan, L. et al., 2002: *Pathways; Experiences of Mental Health Services from a User-Led Perspective*, Galway: Pathways Research Group.

Dante Alighieri: *The Divine Comedy. II: Purgatorio*; with translation and comment by John D. Sinclair; New York: Oxford University Press, 1939/1961.

Davis, A., 1996: Giving Choices Means Taking Chances, in: *Care Plan*, June 1996: 15-18.

Dean, Hartley 2002: *Welfare Rights and Social Policy*; Harlow: Pearson Education.

Department of Health and Children, 2000: *National Health Promotion Strategy 2000-2005*, Dublin: Stationery Office.

Dominelli, L., 1996: De-professionalising Social Work: Anti-Oppressive Practice, Competencies and Postmodernism, in: *British Journal of Social Work*, 26(2): 153-175.

Ferguson, H./O'Reilly, M., 2001: *Keeping Children Safe: Child Abuse, Child Protection and the Promotion of Welfare*, Dublin: A.& A. Farmar.

Foucault, M., 1967: *Madness and Civilization: A History of Insanity in the Age of Reason*, London: Routledge.

Gehlen, Arnold, 1942: *Anthropologische Forschung*; Reinbeck 1961.

Goffman, E., 1961: *Asylums – Essays on the Situations of Mental patients and other Inmates*, London: Penguin Books.

Gramsci, Antonio, 1932-35: [Political Ideologies]; in: Gramsci, Antonio: Prison Notebooks; in: Forgacs, David (Ed.): *The Antonio Gramsci Reader. Selected Writings 1916-1935*; London: Lawrence and Wishart, 1999 196-199.

Habermas, Juergen, 1968: Technik und Wissenschaft als «Ideologie». Für Herbert Marcuse zum 70. Geburtstag am 19.VII 1968; in: Habermas, Juergen: *Technik und Wissenschaft als «Ideologie»;* Frankfurt/M.: Suhrkamp, 1968: 48-103.

[13] Come after me and let the people talk. Stand like a firm tower that never shakes its top for blast of wind; for always the man in whom thought springs up over thought sets his mark farther off, for the one thought saps the force of the other.

Herrmann, Peter, 1998: *European Integration between Institution Building and Social Process. Contributions to a Theory of Modernisation and NGOs in the Context of the Development of the EU;* New York: Nova Science.

Herrmann, Peter, forthcoming: *Person Oriented Services and Social Service Providers in Comparative and European Perspective. Current Debates on Changes by Liberalisation in a Perspective of a Theory of Modernisation.*

Herrmann, Peter/Ryan, Deirdre, 2005: Social Services, Ireland, EUrope and the World – 3rd Level Education in Contemporary Ireland (working title) in: Martha Roßmayer and Deirdre Ryan: *Contemporary Trends in the Academic World – Between Social Commitment and Market Performance* (Working Title); New York: Nova Science, forthcoming.

Howe, D., 1992: Child Abuse and the Bureaucratisation of Social Work, in: *Sociological Review* 40(3): 491-508.

Howe, D., 1996: Surface and Depth in Social Work Practice, in: Parton N. (ed) *Social Theory Social Change and Social Work*, London: Routledge.

Humphries, B., 2003: What else Counts as Evidence in Evidence-based Social Work? in: *Social Work Education*, 22(1): 81-91.

Kant, Iammanuel, 1783: Beantwortung der Frage: was ist Aufklaerung?; in: Kant, Immanuel: *Schriften zur Anthropologie, Geschichtsphilosophie, Politik und Paedagogik* 2. Werkausgabe volume XI; Ed.: Wilhelm Weischedel; Frankfurt/M.: Suhrkamp1968: 53-61.

Kemshall, H., 2002: *Risk Social Policy and Welfare*, Buckingham: Open University Press.

Marshall, Tom H, 1950: Citizenship and Social Class; in: *Citizenship and Social Class*; T.H. Marshall/Tom Bottomore; London et altera: Pluto Press1992.

Miller, P./Rose, N., 1986: *The Power of Psychiatry*, Cambridge: Polity.

Parton N. (ed.), 1996: *Social Theory Social Change and Social Work*, London: Routledge.

Parton, N., 1998: Risk, Advanced Liberalism and Child Welfare: The Need to Rediscover Uncertainty and Ambiguity, in: *British Journal of Social Work*, 28: 5-27.

Pilgrim, D./Rogers, A., 1999: *A Sociology of Mental Illness*. Buckingham: Open University Press.

Preston-Shoot, M/Roberts, G/Ver, S., 1998: Social Work Law: from Interaction to Integration, in: *Journal of Social Welfare and Family Law*, 20(1): 65-80.

Ramon, S., 1991: *Psychiatric Hospital Closure: Myths and Realities*, Chapman and Hall.

Reid, W. J./Zettergren, P. 1999: A Perspective on Empirical Research , in: Shaw, I. & Lishman, J. (eds.) *Evaluation and Social Work Practice*, London: Sage.

Rogers, A./Pilgrim, D. 2003: *Mental Health and Inequality*, Hampshire: Palgrave Macmillan.

Rogers, A./Pilgrim, D./Lacey, R. 1993: *Experiencing Psychiatry-users' Views of Services*, Macmillan/Mind.

Ryan, Deirdre/Herrmann, Peter, 2004: Education – Just another Commodity. Exposing the Rhetoric of «Human Capital» in the Light of Social Quality; in: Herrmann, Peter (ed.), 2004: *Utopia between Corrupted Public Responsibility and Contested Modernisation: Globalisation and Social Responsibility*; New York: Nova Science.

Scheff, T., 1966: *Being Mentally Ill*, Chicago: Aldine Press.

Scull, A., 1975: From Madness to Mental Illness; Medical Men as Moral Entrepreneurs, in: *European Journal of Sociology*, 16: 218-261.

Scull, A., 1981: The Decarceration of the Mentally Ill: A critical View, in: Grusky et al. (eds) *The Sociology of Mental Illness*, New York: Rinehart & Winston.

Southern Health Board, 2002: *Focusing Minds.*

Speed, E., 2002: What Exactly is an Emancipatory Methodology? *Paper to National Disability Authority Conference on Disability Research*, Dublin: December.

Szasz, T., 1970: *The Manufacture of Madness*, New York: Harper and Row.

Szasz, T., 1974: *Ideology and Insanity: Essays on Psychiatric De-humanisation of Man*, Harmondsworth: Penguin.

Tanner, D., 1998: The Jeopardy of Risk, in: *Practice*, 10(1): 15-28.

Taylor, C./White, S., 2000: *Practising Reflexively in Health and Welfare*, Buckingham: Open University Press.

Turner, Bryan S., 1990: Outline of a Theory of Citizenship; in: *Sociology. The Journal of the British Sociological Association*; Finch, Janet/Abercombie, Nick (eds.); May 1990: 24/2: 189-217.

van der Maesen, Laurent, et altera 2004: Renewing of the Social Quality Theory and its Indicators; *Internal Working Paper from the work of the ENIQ-Project*; Amsterdam: European Foundation on Social Quality.

Walsh, T., 1997: Current Issues in Irish Social Work Education, *Paper to IFSW/EASSW European Regional Seminar*, Dublin, August 1997.

Webb, S., 2001: Some Considerations on the Validity of Evidence-based Practice, in social work, in: *British Journal of Social Work*, 31(1): 57-79.

White, S., 1996: Regulating Mental Health and Motherhood in Contemporary Welfare Services, in: *Critical Social Policy* 16(1) pp.67-94.

In: Knowledge in Mental Health
Editors: L.Sapouna and P. Herrmann, pp. 25-38
ISBN 1-59454-812-9


*Chapter 2*

# Mental Health Policy, Law and Risk: Finding a Balance between State Paternalism and Citizenship Rights for People with Mental Health Problems

***Jim Campbell,[1] Bill Healy,[2] Lisa Brophy[3]***
[1]The School of Social Work, Queens University Belfast, Northern Ireland.
[2]The School of Social Work and Social Policy, Latrobe University, Melbourne, Australia.
[3] North West Area Mental Health Service, Melbourne, Australia.

## Abstract

Current western mental health law and policy is characterised by a number of sometimes contradictory processes. At one level we find greater policy attention to the needs and rights of service users, yet, at another level a drift towards more control. This chapter will explore developments in these areas in the UK before drawing upon European, US and Australasian literature to highlight the potentially coercive nature of some mental health law and the failure by states to provide compensatory, reciprocal services. In conclusion it will be argued that policy makers and professionals should be involved in challenging discourses in these areas which often limit the citizenship rights of vulnerable clients.

## Introduction

As we move into the twenty-first century, it is important to consider the political, social and professional factors which influence and shape the way that mental health policy and law operates. In the last few decades there appears to have been a drift towards more coercion and control in this area throughout the western world. It would be wrong, however, to imply that these trends are uniform and universal. In some countries there are greater or lesser protections in law for people with mental health problems, but generally, concerns for the rights of mental health service users have been gradually replaced by a more pessimistic vision of the relationship between these citizens and the state, despite some of the policy rhetoric about the need for empowering forms of service delivery. In this chapter we will explore some of these themes by drawing upon our knowledge and experience of law and policy in a variety of international contexts, in the UK, Australasia and continental Europe. In particular we wish to focus on the increasing tendency by states to use coercive powers in the community, not just to manage what is perceived to be dangerous behaviour, but to satisfy concerns about the safety of the public, the management of risk and the support of paternalistic, 'best interests' decision-making. There is an increased lack of tolerance regarding risk, sometimes extended to include deterioration in mental health that may simply be the result of people exercising their right to make choices about treatment compliance. Much of this concern is driven by the need to reduce costly acute and inpatient service usage and find new ways to 'contain' this vulnerable group. In conclusion an appeal is made for citizens, professionals and policy makers to develop a critical awareness of the need to preserve the rights of some of the most vulnerable people in our communities, and to work towards systems which are emancipatory rather than coercive, and focused on need as much as risk.

## Trends in Mental Health Policy and Law

If we briefly examine competing histories on the incarceration of people with mental health problems in the western world, we find a number of perspectives which reflect differing ideologies and discourses. These range from a modernist view, in which the rise of the asylum in the nineteenth century is viewed broadly in terms of social progress (Jones, 1972), to more radical and Marxist approaches (Scull, 1978). Another way of understanding the complex nature of state power in this domain is to contemplate the manner in which key interests are involved in the social construction of types of problems and disabilities (Pilgrim and Rogers, 1999). Within these perspectives lies a range of explanations that are often used to justify the restriction, or expansion, of rights for people with mental health problems.

What seems clear is that, in the last few decades, a particularly influential set of discourses has informed policy, law and practice. They have helped shape the received wisdom that implies that institutional care is largely malevolent and care in the community generally benevolent (Bartlett and Wright, 1999). As a result, one fairly constant feature of many mental health systems has been the decline of the asylum and the shift towards community care and treatment. The most notable early examples of this trend was the exodus from hospitals in the USA which started in the 1950s and in Italy in the 1960s (Prior, 1999; Ramon, 1996). These developments were later to affect policy in the UK and Australasia during the 1980s and 1990s. Available hospital beds in England and Wales have declined steeply from over 150,000 in 1954 to 43,000 in 1993-4 (DoH, 1995). This movement does not, however, imply that involuntary admissions have fallen, on the contrary the numbers of people who enter hospital on a compulsory basis have generally risen throughout Europe. In the case of England and Wales, these have grown from 7.2% of all admissions for the year 1987/8 to 11.6% for the year 1997/8 (in Hatfield and Antcliff, 2001). It is worth noting international variations at this point, for example it has been estimated that the rate of involuntary admissions in England and Wales at the end of the twentieth century is twice that of Italy (Szmuckler and Holloway, 2000). Prior (1999: 145) has estimated that on average around 10-15% of all admissions in Europe are carried out on a compulsory basis. Parallel trends can be found in Australia, where there have been consistent increases in the number of people being treated involuntarily – both via admission to inpatient units and Community Treatment Orders (CTOs are an important legal mechanism of control which we will discuss in detail below), as well as a significant decrease in the average number of days spent in hospital. In the state of Victoria, for instance, there has been a 23 per cent increase in the total number of involuntary admissions from July 1995 to September 2000 (Auditor-General Report, 2002). Another factor that seems to have been consistent across the UK, Australia and New Zealand is the relative under-funding of mental health services that have not been sufficiently developed to deal with the growing numbers of people not living in institutional settings. The rise in compulsory admissions to psychiatric hospitals can be partly viewed as a perverse outcome, born of failures by governments to finance community services. A conundrum then exists: if people with mental health problems are not supported in the community, they are more likely to relapse and become hospitalised, then quickly discharged because of a shortage of bed space – a phenomenon which has become known the 'revolving door syndrome'.

The acceleration of hospital ward closures has also coincided with debates about dealing with problems that arise when those who have been discharged have been left in the community, often unsupported. This is partly an inevitable consequence of the policy failures described above, and broader structural inequalities faced by service users. People with mental health problems are much more likely to suffer from a range of deprivations in terms of housing, income maintenance and access to the labour market, but they also experience social isolation and stigma: "...people with mental disorders are often doubly excluded from society – in the first instance, as members of disadvantaged groups and in the second, as deviants from what is regarded as normal social behaviour" (Prior, 2001:25-26). In addition to these generally unfavourable circumstances and prospects, these citizens have increasingly been subject to greater state surveillance and control, not just on the basis that they may be a risk, or in need of care themselves, but that they may also pose a threat to the wider community. Later in the chapter we wish to argue that the relationship between adequate service provision and the use of legal sanctions for people with mental health problems is of crucial importance to citizenship rights in this field, but first let us examine the drift towards legal coercion and control in the community.

## Control, Treatment and Care in the Community

If the developments highlighted above can be viewed in terms of rational policy responses to a sustained period of deinstitutionalization, many questions remain about the way in which the state deals with risk and control in the community, and how policies can be maintained at the potential expense of damage to the civil and human rights of clients with mental health problems. It is useful at this point to trace the different approaches in dealing with such issues. In the wider European context there is some variation in the way in which compulsory admission to hospital takes place. A number of states (Belgium, Italy, the Netherlands, Portugal and Greece) insist on an initial judicial process prior to hospitalisation (Prior, 1999: 148) whereas Scandinavian countries tend to engage in a relatively quick involvement of the judiciary, after psychiatrists have made a decision to admit (Hatfield and Ancliffe, 2001: 138). Prior (1999) has argued that there is an increasing European trend towards the protection of the rights, not just by introducing judicial processes, but also through the use of systems of advocacy and by insisting that clearer evidence of dangerousness exists at the time of assessment.

Yet in many Anglo-American jurisdictions, the trend has been towards increasing levels of professional and legal control in the community. This has been justified on the grounds that patients are 'helped' to gain insight into irrational thoughts and behaviour, their quality of life may improve and compulsory admission to hospital is prevented. In the USA, for example, thirty-five states use the mechanism of involuntary Out Patient Commitment (OPC) under the following conditions:

"OPC statutes require compliance with recommended treatment excluding forced medication in the outpatient setting. Under OPC, the responsible clinician may request that law officers escort the non-adherent patient to a community mental health centre for examination and hopeful persuasion to accept treatment." (Swanson et al, 2000:3).

A number of authors (Hiday, 2003; Swanson et al, 2001; Swartz et al, 1998) suggest that OPCs may be effective for some groups of people with mental health problems, particularly those with serious mental illnesses and at risk of violence, but effectiveness is enhanced when combined with regular outpatient appointment attendance and other services. Those professionals who have used Guardianship procedures under UK mental health legislation will recognize the tenor of the language around OPCs, to "require", and to "hopefully persuade" clients to accept treatment. There may be some implied notion of compulsion to such mechanisms but they fall short of a forced use of medication and other interventions in community settings. Over the last decade, however, a more explicit notion of legal compulsion has been operationalised, at first in Australia, and later in New Zealand, that of the CTO. A version of a CTO was introduced in the state of Victoria, Australia, in 1988 following a revision of the Mental Health Act, 1986 [Vic] (Healy and Brophy, 2002). Five broad criteria must be fulfilled before such compulsory powers are used:

- The person must appear to be mentally ill,
- The person's mental illness must require immediate treatment that can be obtained using a CTO,
- That the mental illness creates issues around health, safety and public protection,
- The person has refused treatment, and
- Alternative treatment is not available in a less restrictive setting.

There are a range of safeguards designed to protect the rights of individuals who would be subject to compulsory treatment in the community, for instance through an appeal system which involves a tribunal. However, the purpose, efficacy and ethical justification for such law has been hotly debated in the literature. A number of authors have sought to justify the use of CTOs in terms of reductions in hospitalization, shorter hospital stays, access to support and treatment services, and improved familial relationships (Jaworoswski and Guneva, 2000; O'Reilly; 2002, Power, 1999; Hiday, 2003; Dawson and Romans, 2001). It has also been argued that, in some cases, the use of CTOs may help patients gain insight and thus increase compliance with medication (McIvor, 1998) and that they can help with the management of risk (Freckleton, 1998). Although questions have been raised about the adequacy of the evidence for effectiveness of CTOs (Carney, 2003), some authors have indicated that specific groups may be more likely to be placed on CTOs and suffer as a result (Dawson and Romans, 2001; Rolfe, 2001). In addition to the empirical evidence for and against the efficacy of CTOs, a number of philosophical and legal positions have been taken up. A long-standing issue facing those interested in the subject of therapeutic jurisprudence is to find coherent legal principles to support psychiatric judgement in this area (Rosenhan, 1998). The implication is that if there are fundamental problems of definition about terms as anomalous as mental illness and risk, then it becomes that much more difficult, legally and ethically, to justify interventions which are so coercive. In addition, some authors have suggested that the use of CTOs may not in fact lead to better health outcomes (Calsyn et al, 2002) or that other methods, for example assertive outreach, may be more effective (Preston et al, 2002). There may even be negative consequences for mental health workers as they struggle to find sustainable professional and ethical positions in working with clients who are resistant to care and treatment (Wexler and Winick, 1991; Zigmond, 2001). Perhaps most worrying for professional groups is the assumption, reinforced by the decisions of politicians and policy makers, that public safety should be of as much concern as the mental health needs of clients (Szmukler and Holloway, 2000). In the next two sections of this chapter we will use the case studies of the United Kingdom and Australia to illustrate the way in which politicians, policy-makers and professionals have debated and delivered legal controls in the community as a way of managing perceived risk.

## The Case of the United Kingdom

When we examine the two decades since the introduction of the Mental Health Act (England and Wales) 1983 (it is important to note that two other laws also exist in the UK, reflecting the jurisdictions of Northern Ireland and Scotland), it can be asserted that the state has sought to increase its powers of control, and frequently ignored the rights of people with mental health problems. In retrospect, the legislation of the 1980s can be viewed as essentially a product of the policy and social concerns of the 1970s, when there was more optimism about the capacity of professionals to deliver services and protect the rights of clients. Twenty years on, and with so many fewer people being treated in psychiatric institutions, new discourses of risk and dangerousness have emerged; policy and law have developed to reflect these concerns. For example, a number of high court judgements in the 1980s denied attempts by psychiatrists to use 'long leash' measures which would allow quick re-admissions to hospitals (*Regina v Hallstrom, Gardiner*). Since then, governments have introduced other mechanisms to manage perceived dangerousness. In the 1990s supervision registers, after-care under supervision orders and the Mental Health (Patients in the Community) Act (1995) were introduced in England and Wales. During this period, policy-makers were also involved in attempts to deal with many vulnerable people who lacked capacity and were *de facto* detained in institutions, without reference to due process (*R v. Bournewood Community and Mental Health NHS Trust*).

One of the problems with British mental health policy during this period, despite recent improvements in systems of planning (for example through the Care Programme Approach and the National Services Framework), has been the gaps in provision for people being discharged from hospital, without follow-up. Thus social care staff, often employed by local authorities, have faced difficulties in delivering a seamless service with other professional colleagues – psychiatric nurses, psychologists and psychiatrists – who are largely employed by health authorities. These administrative limitations have, in part, contributed to the many homicides and suicides associated with people who have mental health problems, in the last few decades (Reith, 1998). In this context the current law appears ill-equipped to care, treat and control citizens who have mental disorders and who may be at risk in the community (Bean, 2001). The Richardson Committee (DoH, 1999) that was tasked to review the Mental Health Act in England and Wales established a number of principles which, it was argued, should be used to weigh the power of the state with the rights of people with mental health problems in any new legislation: the law should seek to ensure that patients would not be discriminated against; there should be a balance between the powers of compulsion to be used by professionals and client entitlement to services and resources; in acknowledging the administrative gaps between local and health authorities, the Committee argued that these organisations should have parallel duties to deliver appropriate standard-based services.

However, the expectations that the state should be contracted to offer rights to care and treatment for those people subject to excessive state control in the community were not realised in the subsequent White Paper (DoH, 2000). Instead, a central focus of the proposed legislation has been a concern about dangerousness and risk to the public (Bean, 2001). The White Paper sought to extend the types of mental disorders that could be subject to compulsory treatment to include people with severe personality disorders and those with mental health problems who physically or sexually abuse others. A clear distinction was to be made between the patient's mental health and treatment interests (for example through the development of a care plan), and a public safety interest (which would involve setting out a plan for the management of risks associated with the mental disorder). Of these criticisms, a number are directed at the way in which the government wishes to deal with people with mental health problems who are perceived to be dangerous. A major issue which faces the state in drafting such legislation is in defining what is meant by a mental disorder and risk or dangerousness; such definitions will determine how the rights of vulnerable citizens are preserved or compromised. The European Convention on Human Rights (ECHR) and the European Court of Human Rights have established some principles in legally sanctioning the deprivation of liberty on grounds of mental disorder, although this has not been carried out without some difficulty. It has been suggested that both the ECHR and the UK Human Rights Act have had, to date, little impact on the mental health laws of nation states. One of the problems associated with the ECHR on this subject is that the continued use of the rather outdated term 'unsoundness of mind' is of little help in coming to a concrete definition. The effect has been to allow national states, and in particular psychiatrists, to develop their own terminology, either in legislation or codes of practice (*Winterwerp v Netherlands*). This often implies deference to psychiatric expertise (Gostin, 2000). In the case of the review of the proposed legislation for England and Wales, there have been major concerns expressed about the overly inclusive and indiscriminatory definition of mental disorder proposed by the government. Although the Richardson Committee suggested a definition of mental disorder which was fairly explicit, and excluded disorders of sexual preference or misuse of alcohol or drugs, these exclusions do not appear in the White Paper, which suggests that they may, indeed, be used in future legislation and codes of practice.[1] The government has also attempted to widen the net even further to include offenders with mental disorders and people with severe personality disorders. These proposals have been made despite the criticism that a reconstructed system of mental health review tribunals may not offer sufficient safeguards to protect the ever-expanding groups of people who will be 'captured' by the legislation (Grounds, 2001). A related, and crucially important issue is that of 'capacity'. As Szmuckler and Holloway (2000) have argued, most recent mental health laws in the west are posited upon the principle that involuntary care or treatment should be administered where mental incapacity is proven and when a judgment is confirmed that treatment is in the best interests of the individual. What they criticise is the move away from this important autonomy principle in the proposed legislation; additional criteria based on another principle – the protection of others – has now to be considered in assessments. As they put it: "Removal of the capacity criterion, while leaving a broad definition of mental disorder and the ability to 'treat' purely for the protection of others, leaves enormous scope for abuse." (Szmuckler and Holloway, 2000:199). It has been insisted that in the proposed mental health act a more coherent approach is necessary to the integration of new legislation on incapacity, and also a retreat from the intention to remove 'best interest' and 'therapeutic benefit' tests for people who are solely at risk to themselves (Royal College of Psychiatrists, 2002).

## The Case of Australia

At a time when the review of law in the UK is pointing towards more explicit legal controls in the community, the state has had such powers for over a decade in Australia. Mental Health services in Australia are the responsibility of state and territory governments. However since 1992 they, together with the Commonwealth government, have participated in the development of a national mental health policy and plan (Meadows and Singh, 2002), coinciding with a period in which services were brought out from the era of segregative control and into 'mainstream' health services. As a consequence, there has been a substantial shift in the locus and focus of mental health services from an institutional to a community paradigm. Although there is some variation across jurisdictions, these services are now essentially deinstitutionalised (Carney, 2003). At the same time, despite much discussion and a major national inquiry (Human Rights and Equal Opportunity Commission, 1993), there have been no similar developments in legislation and as a result there are still eight Mental Health Acts in place across the country. Nonetheless, it is possible to identify a pattern of legislative developments that are paralleled across these jurisdictions, albeit occurring at different stages. Law and policy during the decades which followed the Second World War essentially privileged the authority of professionals, and medical staff in particular were empowered to make judgements about compulsory care and treatment in the absence of any independent review process. From about the mid-1970s to the mid-1980s, states began to enact new mental health laws in recognition that statute was lagging significantly behind developments in other international contexts. A number of reviews recommended the

[1] Victorian legislation has 13 specific exclusion criteria that include sexual preference, anti- social personality disorder and misuse of drugs and alcohol.

incorporation of various explicit rights-based principles and definitions in mental health legislation. These included concepts such as a need for treatment', 'dangerousness' and 'least restrictive alternatives'. This move to a stronger rights base in legislation was reflected in the public policy context by the first National Mental Health Plan, which included among its priority concerns consumer rights and legislative reforms (Rees, 2003: 33). The plan set the policy framework for shifting services into the community and the accelerated closure of large institutions.

Australian jurisdictions made an early decision, relative to other international comparators, to enable professionals to use compulsory powers in the community, reflecting institutional closures and the concentrations of services outside large psychiatric hospitals. CTOs are an explicit and direct expression of this policy. Under Australian Mental Health Acts, this state power is vested in the person of a psychiatrist, typically referred to as the 'authorised psychiatrist' who may, without reference to anyone else, revoke an order, detain the person in a acute admission ward and enforce treatment. Appeal to or review by the relevant tribunal is only available after the event and the tribunal may only make a recommendation in the context of compliance with the criteria for establishing involuntary status. Treatment is not a matter for review or appeal and, not surprisingly, it is very rare that such psychiatric decisions are overturned. For instance, in 2002 in the cases determined by the Mental Health Review Board for Victoria only 6.2% of patients were discharged from their involuntary status. Though further research is warranted, it would appear that in Australia, on available data, there is still an overwhelming reliance on medical judgements and practices as the benchmark for decisions about treating psychiatric patients against their wishes. A complicating factor is the variation in state and territory Acts. Tribunals operate within different principles, which may well affect the rights of patients, depending on which jurisdiction they live in:

> "The notion of universal rights for people with mental illness looks ludicrous on consideration of how different rights are depending on the state or territory. A person may or may not be able to challenge the use of ECT at a tribunal, ask the tribunal to draw up a treatment plan, get transcripts of a hearing, have a lawyer represent them, or have a hearing at all before being discharged from hospital, depending on where they are within Australia." ( Delaney, 2003, p71).

More generally, Carney (2003) makes the point that even through a limited and rather generous self-rating process of the national audit of rights under mental health legislation, the level of compliance in both content and practice is at least questionable and in some instances seriously at odds with UN principles on the rights of people with mental health problems. He goes so far as to speculate that, as the focus of the audit subtly shifted from poor performance to best practice it is, "...perhaps presaging the disappearance of rights dialogue from the most recent plans and audit review reports." (Carney, 2003, p14). As a result of such anomalies in both the law and related practices, it is difficult to generalise about the purpose and impact of legal forms of control in the community.

It is useful, nonetheless, to use the case example of the State of Victoria to illustrate some of the policy issues and practice dilemmas which have arisen over the last few decades. There is broad agreement that in Victoria there is a reasonable standard of service provision and it is a place where the experience of implementation of the Act is sufficiently long (approximately

16 years) to have accumulated a body of knowledge to discuss the merits of CTOs. The Victorian Mental Health Review Board began hearings in 1987 and has seen its workload increase enormously in the ensuing 15 years.

> "Over the period 1987-88 to 2000-01, the number of cases scheduled to come before the Board increased by 607%, while the number of cases actually completed by the Board increased by 574%." (Auditor General, Victoria, 2002:108)

These figures are one measure of the degree to which CTOs have become a 'treatment of choice' for many psychiatric patients (Ring et al, 2001), and have in practice moved a long way from their original purpose of maintaining some degree of continuity of treatment as patients left the psychiatric hospital, or in preventing hospital admission. The magnitude of hospital closures has, of course, played a part in the increased use of involuntary detention provisions in the community. A related point which is sometimes made by professionals in this context is that CTOs can ensure a right and access to treatment which would not necessarily be the case in 'normal', voluntary service delivery. It is the other side of this contract between citizen and state which concerns come critics, however. The formal legislation stands up reasonably well to a rights test, but professional practices in the mental health system are significantly less reviewed, researched and evaluated (Carney 2003), with the result that the grey area of consent is not fully acknowledge and sustained:

> "Rights issues loom large at this point for there is a set of conflicting principles which on the one hand establish the need for treatment (protection, duty of care, best interests) whilst on the other hand there is the issue of the right to refuse treatment (principles of autonomy, competence and capacity to consent) and therefore the question of what are the appropriate limits to involuntary treatment." (Healy and Brophy, p 234)

Policy debates, especially those within funding and provider groups, mostly avoid or at worse ignores these problems, and the most recent Victorian policy document for instance makes almost no comment upon such issues (Vic Govt, 2002). Not surprisingly policy discourses have tended to influence operational levels of the mental health system and are more likely to express the concerns of public bureaucrats and views of psychiatrists about efficiency and efficacy. The consequence for mental health service users can be problematic; in particular the complexity of legal and professional ethics may not be acknowledged, leading to excessive concerns about control and risk management:

> "Despite the humanitarian ethos that appears to underpin such shifts from hospital to community-based treatment, CTOs imply considerable state power over the lives of the individuals involved. Consumers face a range of actual and potential threats to their rights." (Brophy et al, p 157)

## Conclusion: Compulsory Care in the Community and the Citizenship Rights of Service Users

This chapter began by providing a review of historical, policy and legal contexts that help explain the shift towards the greater control of people with mental health problems who are living in the community. What emerges from these debates is a range of positions that provide some guidance about possible benefits and drawbacks in using methods of compulsion in the community. Mental health policies in the UK and Australia have involved processes in which service users are increasingly being subject to increased professional surveillance and legal control. For example, it can be asserted that the most controversial proposal in new mental health legislation in the UK is the intention to introduce the types of CTOs which have existed for some years in Australia and New Zealand. On the face of it, there may be good reasons for such policies if it can be shown that therapeutic or other benefits may accrue for the service user – one of the points we made at the start of this chapter was that many of the changes to mental health law in recent years were driven by concerns about existing inadequacies of institutional care.

Yet it is important to note that, although some mental health service user groups believe that involuntary treatment in the community may help in certain contexts, many are hostile to such an extension of state powers (Pinfold and Bindman, 2001). Such views may be seen in the context of long-standing, largely negative experiences of mental health service delivery and law, exacerbated by the fact that much professional activity in this area tends can be paternalistic and potentially oppressive (Braye/Preston-Shoot, 1995:82-83). Although the majority of people who enter the psychiatric hospital do so on a voluntary basis, for those who enter the system against their wishes it is often a traumatic and damaging encounter which erodes citizenship rights (Campbell, 1996; Rodgers et al, 1993). Bradley et al (1995) found that half of a group of patients compulsorily admitted to psychiatric hospital had not been informed of their right of appeal to a mental health tribunal. Similarly, in Australia, there in consistent criticism of the degree to which patients' rights are respected and, furthermore, there are limited mechanisms of complaint, leaving much abuse of power ignored and a resultant community complacency (Carney, 2003; HREOC, 1993).

If it can be agreed that current trends towards more coercive mental law, often based in community settings, are becoming more common in western states, a question arises about how the rights of service users can be protected and state power monitored and modified under these circumstances. This is particularly important, given the less than satisfactory history of care and treatment within prior mental health systems. To begin with, the commonly cited principle of 'least restrictive alternative' should always govern professional and policy-making activity in every case. In view of what service users and carers tend to request at times of distress, the focus of government, agency and professional activity should always be directed at developing protective systems of support for clients and their families at times of need and crisis in the community, rather than an unnecessary, further extension of state power. The use of state control can sometimes be viewed as a symptomatic failure of policy; mental health service users often view the lack of well-funded community-based resources as the underlying issue for many of their problems. Attention to this area by the state would prevent admissions and re-admissions, and avoid the need for recourse to law. In particular, properly staffed, twenty-four-hour crisis teams are favoured by service users and carers in the UK (Sayce et al, 1994; Johnston and Thornycroft, 1995). It may also be the case that, in some jurisdictions, existing mechanisms for care and treatment in the community could provide sufficient powers of control and management for vulnerable people, for example through the strengthening of existing guardianship procedures in the UK. Other innovative approaches might include advance statements or agreements with people who may be predicted to become unwell and at risk (Atkinson and Garner, 2002; Papageorgiou et al., 2002). Again, such mechanisms depend on available resources and a commitment by professionals to communicate and engage effectively with clients.

On the other hand, if Community Care and Treatment Orders become part of new mental health legislation in the UK, as seems likely, it is important that sound ethical principles and practices are enshrined in the legislation and codes of practice. The incoming Scottish legislation, for example, sets out stringent tests for admission to compulsory care, all of which must be satisfied: there must be a presence of mental disorder, such that the necessary care and treatment cannot be provided by agreement with the patient; the person's decision-making capacity is impaired; the treatment is likely to benefit the patient; the treatment is the least restrictive alternative compatible with safe and effective care; and there is significant risk of harm to the health or safety of the patient or a significant risk of harm to other persons if such a treatment is not administered. The centrality of the capacity test, alongside a more exclusive definition of mental disorder, as well as plans to introduce patient advocacy and other supportive services, suggests that this legislation is more progressive than the proposed bill for England and Wales. These safeguards should encourage professionals to consider the primacy of service users' rights and be less preoccupied with public safety.

The examination of other international experiences of involuntary treatment in the community can be helpful and informative. For example, in New Zealand, an additional protection for mental health service users is the involvement of a judge who must be satisfied that outpatient treatment is appropriate and available (Dawson/Romans, 2001). In contrast, lessons can be learnt from the example of the Mental Health Review Board for Victoria, Australia, and its lack of powers to comment on standards of treatment.[2] Mental health law in itself, however, will not guarantee citizenship rights for service users if professionals do not practice in enlightened, empowering ways. Case workers have an important part to play in providing mental health review boards with holistic assessments of risk and management as well, as contributing to more humane approaches to the compulsory care and treatment of people with mental health problems (Brophy et al, 2003). Furthermore, as the debate continues regarding effectiveness, current attention needs to also be given to the adequate preparation of staff of all disciplines in order that the potential negative impact of coercion is minimised (Simpson, 2003). Hiday (2003) has argued that client resistance to compulsory care and treatment will be minimised if recipients believe that the process is fair and respectful, and feel validated and listened to. The adequacy of treatment is also an important issue – both in honouring the principle of offering reciprocity of care and treatment when such significant curtailing of rights takes place. It is also clear that adequate resources need to be made available, not just for people who are compulsorily detained, but for many other vulnerable individuals with mental health problems who may be at the cusp of state intervention.

---

2 Recently announced amendments to the Mental Health Act (1986) Vic address this issue and in future the MHRB will be able to comment on the adequacy of treatment.

The citizenship rights of people with mental health problems have for long periods in history been damaged by social attitudes and political strategies which were often ill-informed and which tended to disregard service user views. At the start of the new century, there are opportunities to affect mental health law and policy at a range of levels – international, national and local. Current debates about the efficacy and purpose of involuntary treatment in the community can be influenced by a range of constituencies – lawyers, mental health professionals, the wider public and of course the very citizens who are subject to control. We believe that it is not possible to stand back from these debates; to ignore them would be to leave the field open to those who would be less interested in using holistic perspectives to understand the complex causes and solutions to mental health problems.

## Acknowledgements

We wish to acknowledge the kind assistance provided by the Wellcome Trust in providing a travel grant to carry out research which was used in part of this chapter.

## References

Atkinson, J.M./Garner, H.C. (2002): Least Restrictive Alternative – Advance Statements and the New Mental Health Legislation; in: *Psychiatric Bulletin*, 26:7, 246-251.

Auditor-General Victoria (2002): *Mental Health Services for People in Crisis*; Melbourne: Government Printer for the State of Victoria.

Bartlett, P./Wright, D. (eds.) (1999): *Outside the Walls of the Community*; London: Athlone.

Bean, P. (2001): *Mental Disorder and the Community*; London: Palgrave.

Bradley, C./Marshall, M./Gath, D. (1995): Why do so Few Patients Appeal Under Section 2 of the Mental Health Act?; in *British Medical Journal*, 310, 346-7.

Braye, S./Preston-Shoot, M. (1993): *Empowering Practice in Social Care*; Buckingham: Open University Press.

Brophy, L./Campbell, J./Healy, B. (2003): Dilemmas in the Case Manager's Role: Implementing Involuntary Treatment in the Community; in: *Psychiatry, Psychology and the Law*, 10:1, 154-163.

Calsyn, R./Winter, J./Morse, G (2000): Do Consumers who Have a Choice Have Better Outcomes?; in: *Community Mental Health Journal*. 36(3), 149-160.

Campbell, J. (1999): Mental Health Policy, Care in the Community and Political Conflict: the Case of the Integrated Service in Northern Ireland; in: P. Bartlett and Wright, D. (eds.) *Outside the Walls of the Community*, London: Athlone.

Carney, T. (2003): Mental Health Law in Postmodern Society: Time for New Paradigms?; in: Psychiatry, *Psychology and the Law*. 10: 1, pp. 12-32.

Community Care (2002): Mental Health Alliance Attacks Draft Legislation as Flawed and Unworkable; in: *Community Care*, September 19, 2002, 1440, p.8.

Dawson J./Romans, S. (2001): Uses of CTOs in New Zealand: Early Findings, Australian and New Zealand; in: *Journal of Psychiatry*, 35, 190-195.

Delaney, S. (2003): An Optimally Rights Recognising Mental Health Tribunal – What can be Learned from Australian Jurisdictions; in: *Psychiatry, Psychology and the Law* 10: 1, 71-84.

Department of Health (1995): *Health and Personal Social Services Statistics for England and Wales*; London: HMSO.

Department of Health (1999): *Report of the Expert Committee: Review of the Mental Health Act, 1989: Proposals for Consultation*; London: HMSO.

Department of Health (2000): *Reforming the Mental Health Act*; London: HMSO.

Freckleton, I. (1998): Decision Making about Involuntary Psychiatric Treatment: an Analysis of the Principles Behind Victorian Practice; in: *Psychiatry, Psychology and the Law*, 5(20), 249-264.

Gostin, L. (2000): Human Rights of Persons with Mental Disabilities: The European Convention of Human Rights; in: *International Journal of Law and Psychiatry*, 23: 2, 125-59.

Hatfield, B./Antcliff, V. (2001): Detention under the Mental Health Act: Balancing Rights, Risks and Needs for Services; in: *Journal of Social Welfare and Family Law*, 23(2): 135-154.

Healy, B./Brophy, L. (2002): Law, Psychiatry and Social Work; in Swain, P.A. In the *Shadow of the Law: The Legal Context of Social Work Practice*, NSW, The Federation Press.

Human Rights and Equal Opportunity Commission (1993): Human Rights and Mental Illness: *Report of the National Inquiry into the Human Rights of people with Mental Illness*; Canberra: Australian Government Printing Service.

Jaworoswski, S./Guneva, R. (2002): Decision-making in Community Treatment Orders: A comparison of Clinicians and Mental Health Review Board Members; in: *Australian Psychiatry,*10,1.

Johnson, S./Thornicroft, G. (1995): Emergency Psychiatric Services in England and Wales; in: *British Medical Journal*, 311, 287-8.

Jones, K. (1972): *A History of Mental Health Services*; London: RKP.

Hiday, V. (2003): Coerced Community Treatment: International Trends and Outcomes; in Dielsfeld , K. and Freckleton, I. (2003) *Involuntary Detention and Therapeutic Jurisprudence,* Dartmouth, England: Ashgate.

McIvor, R. (1998): The Community Treatment Order: Clinical and Ethical Issues; in: *Australian and New Zealand Journal of Psychiatry*. 32, 223-228.

Papageorgiou, A. et al (2002): Advance Directives for Patients Compulsorily Admitted to Hospital with Serious Mental Illness; in: *British Journal of Psychiatry*, 181, 513-519.

Pilgrim, D./Rogers, A (1999): A Sociology of Mental Health and Illness; London: Palgrave.

Pinfold, V./Bindman, J. (2001): Is Compulsory Treatment ever Justified?; in: *Psychiatric Bulletin*, 25:7, 268-275.

Preston et al. (2002): Assessing the Outcome of Compulsory Psychiatric Treatment in The Community: An Epidemiological Study in Western Australia; in: *BMJ*, 324, 1244-1249.

Prior, P. (1999): *Gender and Mental Health*; London: Macmillan.

Prior, P. (2001): Protective Europe – Does it Exist for People with Mental Disorders?; in: *Journal of European Social Policy*, 11:1, 25-38.

Rees, N. (2003): International Human Rights and Mental Health Tribunals Obligations; in: *Psychiatry, Psychology and the Law*, 10:1, 33-43.

Reith, M. (1998): *Community Care Tragedies: A Practice Guide to Mental Health Inquiries*; Birmingham: Venture Press.

Ring, D./Brophy, L./Gimlinger, A. (2001): Examining Community Treatment Orders in Victoria: A Preliminary Inquiry into their Efficacy; in: *Health Issues*, 66: 13-17.

Rogers, A., Pilgrim, D. and Lacey, R. (1993): *Experiencing Psychiatry*; London: Macmillan.

Rolfe, T. (2001): *Community Treatment Orders: A Review*; Perth: Office of the Chief Psychiatrist.

Rosenhan, S. (1998): Psychiatrists and Compulsion: a Map of Ethics; in: *ANZJP*, 32: 785-793.

Sayce, L./Christie, Y./Cobb, A./Slade, M. (1994): Users' Perspectives on Emergency Needs; in: M. Phelan, G. Strathdee and G. Thornicroft (eds) *Emergency Mental Health Services in the Community*, Cambridge: Cambridge University Press.

Scull, A. (1977): *Decarceration: Community Treatment and the Deviant*; NJ: Prentice Hall.

Simpson, A. (2003): A Clinical Perspective on Involuntary Outpatient Treatment; Efficacy and Ethics; in: K. Dielsfeld and I. Freckleton, *Involuntary Detention and Therapeutic Jurisprudence*, Dartmouth, England: Ashgate.

Szmukler, G./Holloway, F. (2000): Reform of the Mental Health Act: Health or Safety?; in: *British Journal of Psychiatry*, 177: 196-200.

Swanson, J. et al (2000): Involuntary Out-patient Commitment and Reduction of Violent Behaviour in Persons with Severe Mental Illness; in: *BJP*, 176, 324-331.

Swartz, M.S./Swanson, J.W./Hiday, V.A./Borum, R./Wagner, H.R./Burns, B.J. (1998): Violence and Severe Mental Illness; The Effects of Substance Abuse and non-Adherence to Medication; *American Journal of Psychiatry* 155, 226-231.

Victorian Government Department of Human Services (2002): *New Directions for Victoria's Mental Health Services*; Melbourne: Department of Human Services.

Welxer, D. /Winick, B. (1991): *Essays in Therapeutic Jurisprudence*; Durham, N.C., and U.S.A: Carolina Academic Press.

Zigmond, A.S. (2001): Reform of the Mental Health Act 1983: The Green Paper; in: *Psychiatric Bulletin*, 25: 126-128.

In: Knowledge in Mental Health
Editors: L.Sapouna and P. Herrmann, pp. 39-55 ISBN 1-59454-812-9


*Chapter 3*

# RISK AVOIDANCE AND RISK TAKING IN MENTAL HEALTH SOCIAL WORK

***Shulamit Ramon***
Interprofessional Health and Social Studies, School of Community Health and Social Studies, Anglia Polytechnic University, Cambridge, UK

## ABSTRACT

This chapter will look at issues related to risk in mental health social work, especially the over-focus on risk avoidance and the need to create space for calculated risk taking. Examples from Britain and continental Europe will be utilised.

## INTRODUCTION

The discourse on risk in British mental health social work (MHSW), and beyond it into the multidisciplinary context, is presently prolific. Nearly all of it focuses on *risk avoidance*. This focus can be observed in training for MHSW, research, policy and legislation.

This is less so in continental Europe. We therefore need to understand better the factors underlying the British preference, which largely omits serious consideration of *risk taking* in its policy and practice.

This chapter will explore the above-mentioned issues, and look at some relevant practice examples from the perspectives of social workers, mental health service users and their carers.

## THE GENERIC RISK DISCOURSE

The discourse about risk does not emanate from the mental health system. Conceptually it is located in the debate about freedom and control, citizenship, crime and deviance, health and illness, with modernity and postmodernity (Giddens, 1991, Beck, 1992, Furedi, 1997, Rose, 2000). Its protagonists argued that each Western society copes with the increased uncertainty, which has been brought about by the growing gap between technological development and social fallibility, by increasing risk control, or by avoiding it. Thus control has become a synonym of avoidance. These eminent writers see risk control as an extension of social control, something to be lamented but to be taken for granted.

One does not need to disagree with the assumption of increasing, and ever more refined, social control to notice that risk is never considered in their discourse as worth taking individually and socially, as a buzz which stimulates people to give their best to a shared objective. Instead, the focus is on the increase in visible and less visible means of social control as an inevitable consequence of living with uncertainty.

This position goes against the grain of everyday life in the same societies in which ordinary people admire risk taking by a minority, and at times have a go at it themselves. Although a cliché, it is virtually impossible to live by adhering only to risk avoidance as a major strategy for living, without the utilisation of risk taking as a complimentary framework. This applies to the most banal risk such as crossing the road, extending to the more serious risks such as choosing a partner, or whether to be operated on when seriously ill. Some would go further to say that life is not worth living if it does not have some elements of risk taking, which put the spice of excitement into living. While some risk taking is what makes non-conforming or even illegal behaviour seen as worthwhile taking, most risk taking behaviour is within the narrow legal boundaries and the wider ones of conformity.

As a society we admire some types of risk taking, such as:

- Mountain climbing
- Explorers to unknown territories
- Marathon runners
- Diving
- Motor racing
- Writing a first successful novel
- Business gambling which pay off
- Inventors who risk all but succeed in becoming famous and successful
- Surgeons
- "Falling in love"

Moreover, these sociological approaches to risk negate the fact that risk taking also offers *the promise of new opportunities to become what one feels s/he has the potential to be*. This is well analysed by Harry Ferguson (2001) in his paper *"Social work, individualisation and life politics"*.

Interested in emancipatory politics, Ferguson looks at how the lack of permanency in life in our time offers us also more diverse options, such as different types of intimate relationships, work, leisure and communication. All of these choices necessitate a greater degree of personal responsibility.

In his framework, a normal biography *can* become:

- the elective biography
- the reflexive biography
- the do-it-yourself biography
- the "tight-rope" biography

While aware that the possibilities we can exercise are limited by our past and present history, we have also become more aware that we usually have more than one option at most junctions in our life, and that to make a choice a reality risk would need to be taken. These risks can be financial (e.g. re-mortgaging our house to take a trip around the world); social (loss of status if we opt for a lower ranked occupation, a partner of the same sex); physical (being an explorer entails at times physical endurance); and psychological (the success of a first novel cannot be assured; moving to another country can lead to isolation). Yet more people are ready to take these risks for the sake of turning their dreams into reality. Thus life at present has become more risky for most people, in part due to the opening up of more possibilities for them to choose from.

It could be argued that the increase in possibilities also leads to increased stress levels, and inevitably to an increase in ill mental health, as it undermines the sense of coherence we need in order to live at peace with ourselves and others. Yet we know from the world of work that taking risk while *being in control* enables people to do more, do it better, and be more able to innovate (Bunce and West, 1996).

## MENTAL HEALTH RISK DISCOURSE

The risk discourse is particularly developed within Anglo-Saxon societies, where it is assumed that the ideology of individual freedom and autonomy is based on *regulation from within,* in which those who do not conform are regulated through a series of inclusionary and exclusionary mechanisms and processes. Prominent writers (e.g. Rose, 2000) further assume that the inclusionary discourse of people with disabilities (e.g. inclusion within education and employment), including those with mental illness, is no more than an attempt to ensure their conformity and hence the reduction of risk to their society and to themselves. Within this perspective, empowerment is no more than a fiction and a con, because it is aimed to offer the illusion of being in control over one's life, when one is merely toeing the line in terms of being a good – i.e. conforming – citizen.

Given this line of argument, it is not surprising that people who embody mental illness are perceived only as a threat to social cohesion and hegemony. Professionals working with them are seen as mandated to ensure the reduction of the threat, the return to the fold of responsible, self-regulated citizens, and if this is not possible then the application of exclusionary sanctions follows. The fascination within post-modernity with courting the irrational in particular, as expressed in literature, films, plays, poetry and the visual arts, has escaped the notice of these sociologists, as did emphatic approaches to understanding mental illness and the (temporary) excitement/liberation it offers – side by side with suffering – to those experiencing it. Even the possibility of the co-existence of threat with excitement is not recognised, let alone that of crediting users with having valuable expertise in experiencing this ambiguity to offer to the rest of us.

There are *important* reasons for focusing on risk avoidance in mental health, which include:

- Fear of others being hurt by people suffering from ill mental health.
- Fear of harm to self due to mental ill health.
- Media coverage of mental health users and of professional activities has focused mainly on homicide, and a little on suicide, by users.
- Politicians are very sensitive to issues related to public protection.
- Professionals have responded to the media and the politicians' stand by becoming defensive and have been instructed to assess and manage risk avoidance.
- As a result of the above, fear of the unpredictable element in some mental illness has been extended to all mental ill health categories.

Politicians in the Western world are perceiving risk policies and measures as one of the two most important core issues of mental health policy, the other being *cost containment* (Shera, Healy, Aviram and Ramon, 2002). The current debate in the UK on the proposals for the introduction of community treatment orders (CTOs) and of the preventive removal from the community of people diagnosed as having antisocial personality disorder highlights the direction in which the British government wishes to go, following that of many North American states and Australia (Brophy, Campbell and Healy, 2003, Hiday and Scheid-Cook, 1989, Home Office and the Department of Health,1999). Continental Europe has not gone down the same route as the English-speaking world in terms of risk avoidance. None of the EU countries apart from Britain has legislated for CTOs, and the issue of risk avoidance does not seem to preoccupy their politicians, professionals or informal carers. The statistics of self harm and harm to others are often unreliable, but there is little to suggest that the rate of such incidents is lower in other Western European countries. Some of them – e.g. the Netherlands and the Scandinavian countries – have more developed alternatives to hospitalisation in a crisis, while others do not (e.g. Spain, France, Germany, Greece). Some countries – such as Italy – have developed more extensive methods of both solidarity and attention to underlying social issues, even though the level of financial benefits is lower than in Northern Europe. These approaches explain some of the reasons for the relative lack of interest in risk avoidance, but not all. There is some evidence that the media in Italy demonises people with severe mental illness less than in the UK (Ramon and Savio, 2000).

British MHSWs are the only group among social workers in Europe to have extended legal power and duties pertaining to risk avoidance in mental health. Since the introduction of the role of the Approved Social Worker (ASW) in 1983, ASWs have had to focus on their role in compulsory admission, which entails assessment through interviewing and documentary evidence, and reaching the decision as to whether to recommend such an admission or not in the light of availability of the least restrictive alternatives to hospitalisation, in conjunction with the decisions taken by psychiatrists and GPs (Barnes, Bowel, Newton and Fisher, 1990).

Insufficient time is left to engage even in the other tasks required by the legislation, such as following up clients, let alone in risk taking professional activities. While in the majority of cases the social worker is likely to recommend compulsory admission when a request for assessment has been made, in those minority cases in which the social worker does not recommend compulsory admission, s/he has to calculate – and take – the risk of what will happen to the client, to relatives and friends near to him/her, and to unknown others without such an admission. S/he needs also to calculate at any such application for compulsory admission the risk to the client from the admission itself – his/her self and social identity, relationships with others, the deprivation of civil rights during the admission, and the likelihood of drifting into a cycle of admissions and chronicity.

Care managers in countries such as Australia, Britain and Canada – likely to be social workers or nurses – collate evidence on risk and make decisions as to the boundaries of everyday life activities of service users.

Risk taking and risk avoidance issues are particularly acute for those, such as assertive outreach teams, or voluntary sector organisations (e.g. Turning Point, a British organisation focused on personalised work in the community with people who have mental illness and/or addiction). They are working with clients described as "hard to engage" in the community – people who have opted not to be in touch with statutory mental health services, usually after years of unsatisfactory contact from their perspective, who are nevertheless assessed as having serious mental health difficulties, and often also have substance misuse problems too.

In a recent study of four Turning Point projects, the key workers expressed their concerns about being on their own with the clients, while praising the ethos of the service and being mainly satisfied with the work they willingly engage with (Ramon, 2003b).

A recent research project (Williams, 2002) has highlighted the low morale among ASWs and the shortage in numbers in the north of England. If anything, one can predict that the situation in the rest of the country is at most no better, and is probably much worse in London, where the number of applications for compulsory admission is higher than elsewhere. The study does not go on to analyse the reasons for the low morale beyond the cumulative impact of an insufficient number of ASWs. I would argue that in addition to this burden, it is the nature of focusing on one narrow aspect of mental health work which contributes significantly to the low morale.

While ASW work has given MHSW more power (albeit largely of coercive nature), higher salary and greater prestige among mental health professionals, in its current stage it has also deprived them of the opportunity of engaging in the more caring, therapeutic, empowering and innovative work of which social workers are capable. Risk taking ranks high among the types of work ASWs have been discouraged from undertaking, as will be discussed below.

MHSW in continental Europe covers a wide range of emphases. In some countries these social workers focus on the financial eligibility of clients; in others they are part of a therapeutic team focusing on in-depth work with users and their families (e.g. Sweden), and/or they engage in building the links with relevant community groups (France, Germany), or in initiating and managing voluntary organisations (The Netherlands).

## Risk Avoidance Practice and Policy Issues for Users

It is important to identify risk avoidance practice and policy issues, as risk taking would be about reversing them in some instances. They include admission to a special environment where the user is under constant observation and supervision and deprived of his/her freedom of movement and association with others. The more confined the setting, the greater the threat to other patients and staff, as well as to the index user, as there are fewer alternatives in which to channel the tension.

Although it is recognised that the more occupied the patient is with pleasant activities the lower the level of risk, little by way of fun or stimulating activities is available in acute admission settings for high risk patients, as distinct from some more long-term secure settings.

Thus the *organisational facet* feeds on unhelpful attitudes and modes of working (Bowers, 2002). An erosion of belief in the value of the system and of professional contribution to it is likely to follow, leading to burn-out and cynicism. Indeed, the rate of staff retention on acute wards and high security services is poor. Consequently, what they offer to users is a distancing, controlling practice.

The importance of the *physical environment* to the sense of safety and consequently to feeling empowered has emerged as one of the most significant dimensions in a study of empowerment components on different wards (acute, rehabilitation, long term), in which the dimensions originated from interviews with users (Schafer, 2003).

Social workers are not usually based in acute admission wards, and hence are spared their impact. However, this turns them into outsiders from the ward staff's and users' perspectives.

The realisation that the high tariff settings are not the most effective ones for the purpose of negative risk reduction has led to the introduction of community treatment orders (CTOs) in Australia (Brophy, et al, 2003), Canada, New Zealand, the United States (Hiday, 1989) and the United Kingdom (Foster, 2002) (where they are currently titled "supervision orders" and "guardianship"). These are compulsory orders focused on where people should live, their presence in intervention settings, their daily activities, the control of their finances, and their entitlement to support additional to that provided to other people with mental health problems who are not subject to these orders. The major sanction for not obeying is a return to hospitalisation.

Mental health service users in all of the countries which have established CTOs of one type or another oppose this new invention, primarily on grounds of the deprivation of civil liberties. They see the CTOs as yet another facet of the *medicalisation* of mental illness as much as a mechanism of greater coercive control, and prefer interventions focused on personalised relationships between staff and users, mutual support, and safe crisis facilities in the community as alternatives to hospitalisation (May, Hartley and Knight, 2003).

*Women* users have been vocal in expressing their views about acute admission wards and high secure hospitals as *unsafe* places for women (Mental Health Media, 2003). When Labour came to power in Britain in 1997, the government promised the end of wards in which accommodation is shared by men and women, and the forced socialisation of women with men on such premises. Thus far, however, little has been achieved in phasing out mixed wards. This raises the issue, which is embarrassing and difficult to confront, of users harming other users, and of a philosophy which women see as harmful.

*Black* users' and carers' associations, and a number of both black and white professionals, have protested since the 1980s against the fact that black people, especially young black men, are more likely to be compulsorily admitted, over-medicated, and less likely to be given talk therapies than white users (Thomas, Stone, Osborn, Thomas and Fisher, 1993).

People to whom a diagnosis of *personality disorder* has been attributed have become the newest group to be stigmatised by the British media, but not in continental Europe. A study in which user researchers with personality disorder interviewed other users with the label has demonstrated this (Ramon, Castillo and Morant, 2001, Castillo, 2002). Most of the respondents reported being treated considerably less well after being given the diagnosis than before. More subtle differences emerge when their own perceptions of their difficulties are compared with the diagnosis. Eighty per cent of the respondents reported depression and impact of child abuse as their major problems, and the same percentage had depression or anxiety attributed as their secondary diagnosis, while having personality disorder as their first (Castillo 2002). It is likely that what has tilted the professional decision in the direction of PD rather than that of depression relates to assumed risk to others and self, coupled with moral apprehension about their socially unacceptable behaviour.

The issue of fear from potential violence lies behind the political agenda in the context of personality disorder. Fear of black young men is more rooted within professional practice, where it is not articulated as it is embarrassing for mental health professionals, many of whom are from ethnic minorities, to admit to accepting racist beliefs. Although women constitute a clear majority of mental health professionals, the overwhelming focus on risk within acute and secure facilities leads to a particular type of blindness to the impact of admission to these same facilities.

## Policy Issues for Carers

A recent study of ASWs, users and the Nearest Relative (NR) (the nominated relative who has some legal powers within the British legislation to ask and agree to compulsory admission and discharge) (Rapaport, 2003) has illustrated the element of poor communication and poor information-giving in potential risk situations between the NRs and the ASWs who have the responsibility to provide this information. This process is taking place against a background of increased tension between users and their relatives, which in part has led to the request for an assessment for compulsory admission, at times to a sense of being betrayed by the users, and being neglected and unheard by the NR, who feels unable to achieve any positive conflict resolution. In addition, the legal information is written in a language incomprehensible by lay people, and receiving it in at a time of crisis is doomed to failure.

Carers perceive professionals' attempts to not share information with them, and to doubt their perspective on what is happening to their family member, as indications of disrespect of their contribution and of attempts to exclude them as key people in this context (Hugman and Pearson, 1995).

Carers in Anglo-Saxon countries seem to welcome CTOs as providing a much needed structure and support. In fact, organisations such as NAMI (National Alliance of the Mentally Ill) in the US have led the demand for CTOs. Yet the largest British carers' organisation, –

Rethink (formally the National Schizophrenia Fellowship) – has opposed the latest proposal to allow preventive hospital detention for people with antisocial personality disorder as a step too far in deprivation of civil liberties.

## RISK TAKING

### Value and Theory Framework

Attention was paid in the introduction to the integral part of risk taking to our lives, and especially to its emancipatory component. Given the justified focus on risk avoidance in the work with people experiencing mental ill health, the question as to the place of risk taking within this context becomes central. Risk taking within mental health is based on values which are an integral part of universally accepted social work values. The theoretical framework and the specific values are embedded in the following:

- The Strengths approach
- Social role valorisation
- The right to self determination
- The right to fail

### The Strengths Approach

This approach was developed in the US by Saleebey (1992) and by Rapp for working with users of mental health services (Rapp, 1998), in the wake of psychiatric hospital closure in the late 1960s and early 1970s. The closure was in part premised on the belief that the resettled patients do not only have weaknesses, but also have abilities and potential that have not been utilised within the institution.

Within this approach the following is assumed:

- The focus is on individual strengths rather than pathology.
- Client-worker relationships are primary and essential.
- Interventions are based on client self-determination.
- Community is viewed as an oasis of resources, not as an obstacle.
- Aggressive outreach is the preferred mode of intervention.
- People suffering from severe mental illness can continue to learn, grow and change.

The focus on strengths rather than on pathology is not a tautology. It is a shift in emphasis which does not deny that people may have difficulties and problems, but accepts that unless we focus simultaneously on the abilities that they possess, we will not manage to reveal the latter and will not motivate users, carers and professional providers to focus on the strengths. This was revolutionary at the time, and remains so for a large number of lay and professionals who are yet to shift from the pathology-only position.

There are consequences of these assumptions in everyday practice, which entail:

- Paying more attention than before to enhancing the individualisation of clients
- Facilitating of partnership rather than adversary
- Fostering empowerment
- Blending societal, programmatic, and client goals

We will look at how these are in fact implemented in the practice examples section.

The protagonists of the strengths approach do not discuss social control or risk taking issues *per se*. The unabashed focus on assertive outreach perhaps indicates that the critique of this intervention as too intrusive in people's lives has either not been heard by them, or has been rejected without an open debate.

## Social Role Valorisation

Social Role Valorisation (SRV) was developed within the field of learning difficulties by Wolfensberger in 1983 (Wolfensberger, 1983). This principle pinpoints disabled people's right to a socially valued place amidst the rest of us. It analyses the tragedy of institutionalisation as one which segregated residents from ordinary living and ordinary people, thus depriving them of opportunities to develop further their social and personal knowledge and skills, and in turn rendering them incapable and thus justifying the stigma attached to their disability by society (Ramon, 1991). The framework takes it for granted that people, including those disabled, have both weaknesses and strengths, abilities and disabilities. Those recognised as disabled may need more support to bring to the fore their abilities, and, for them to have a genuine place, our emphasis on economic success and work prestige needs to be revised to include basic human qualities such a loving and giving.

SRV has developed an audit of services which looks at whether these are enabling or disabling; do away with stigma or perpetuate it in the way they use language in connection with their users; the way the physical environment is giving the message of respect or lack of it; whether users have real choices in what is on offer to them or not. Wolfensberger used harsh words in describing the damage professionals do to disabled people, especially mental health professionals, by treating them as bundles of pathology.

This has impacted on the process and outcomes of psychiatric hospital closure and resettlement in some British settings (Wainwright, 1992), as well as on care management (Brandon D., Atherton, and Brandon A., 1996; Brandon, 1997).

SRV has been criticised as being too white and middle-class in its aspirations for disabled people. Also, it does not have a critical dimension concerning the type of social control which the adherence to a socially valued role brings with it. Issues of risk avoidance, however, have been part of its application to practice with a variety of disabled people. There, risk avoidance has been treated pragmatically, with minimum fuss and maximum respect to the disabled person.

SRV developed initially in Denmark, Sweden and Norway in the late 1950s and early 1960s, under the heading of normalisation and in the field of learning difficulties. Scandinavian social workers have therefore taken for granted this philosophy.

Although Italian social workers were not using the same terminology, the emphasis in the Italian psychiatric reform, from its inception in the late 1960s onwards, on full de-institutionalisation, de-stigmatisation, and full and respectful integration of people with mental illness into the community implied a very similar conceptual and value framework. If anything, the Italian perspective has been less psychologically focused in relation to mental ill health and more preoccupied with removing social barriers to the rehabilitation of people with mental illness, and the disruption of the connections between poverty and mental illness.

## Self-determination and the Right to Fail

The right to self-determination is a core value specific to social work, guiding workers to enable service users to exercise choice as to every aspect of their lives. Rooted in an individualistic and liberal society, the potential conflict with socially desirable choices vs. individual choices has been handled early on in the literature of social work by arguing that there is always a range of choices which are compatible with both demands/requirements. This amounts to accepting social preferences as morally better than individual choices in principle. This principle has been criticised as "naïve" or hypocritical insofar as social workers are only too aware of the many constraints put on clients wanting to exercise their self-determination as against the views of professionals, not to mention constraints which arise out of their family and social background. Yet there are social workers who take this principle seriously and who do their best to enable clients to exercise it (McDermott, 1975).

This right is also a part of the legacy of social work, having been recognised as a principle subsumed under the right to self-determination in social work in Sawyer's 1975 article (Sawyer, 1975). Sawyer argued that it is both difficult and unrealistic to expect clients to grow and develop without taking calculated risks, and without failing from time to time. His argument is echoed in Brandon's writings (1991) for people with mental health problems.

I do not know of any other helping profession which accepts failure as a *right*, rather than as an inevitable price we may pay when our calculated risk-taking strategy has failed. This recognition within social work does not necessarily mean that most social workers enable the exercise of this right, but it does mean that the issue is acknowledged and at times debated. In the original discussion, Sawyer looked at the underlying reasons which prevent social workers from enabling their clients to exercise this right. These include:

- the wish to protect the client from new failure, given that many of them would come with a history of failures;
- the wish to protect one's professional reputation as someone who fosters success and prevents failure;
- the fear that the client will collapse if s/he failed yet again.

All of these reasons are highly relevant within the field of mental health, and underline the focus on risk avoidance. However, those who accept the principles of strengths and SRV would consider that people experiencing mental ill health can take calculated risks with more support than other people would need, rather than that they should not take any risks.

It is only when *calculated* risk taking is allowed to be considered that the right to fail can be exercised. Socially, our attitude to people who fail when they take a risk is less favourable than it should be logically. More often than not they are blamed for miscalculating the risk and therefore for the failure. Often, those who knew them well at the height of their success are ashamed to be seen with them at the time of failure. As a society, it would seem that we are thus afraid of failure.

## TYPES OF RISK TAKING

Risk taking is necessary in each aspect of mental health where the primary purpose is that of improving the quality of life of service users; yet each aspect brings with it somewhat different issues and considerations. A secondary purpose is that of improving the quality of the working life of front-line workers.

Below, I shall look at a number of relevant examples of projects established by British MHSWs, attempting to tease out the issues related to risk taking.

a. *Training and engaging local women* as leaders of groups of isolated women by the Family Welfare Association (FWA) in the 1970s.

   This project was the first to apply the lessons of George Brown's work on the social origins of depression (Brown and Harris, 1978) by training local women in two London boroughs to lead groups of women who were single parents and isolated. The meetings took place at the leaders' homes, and were run as a social event which enabled discussion. Refreshments and child-minding were on offer. The projects were successful in enabling the participants to create their own social networks and thus to reduce the level of isolation and vulnerability by using very modest means.

   Running these groups entailed risk taking for the leaders, the participants, and the social workers at the FWAs who were responsible for them. The main risk taken was believing that a six-week training module was sufficient to enable the lay leaders to run a group of vulnerable people, yet it worked well and empowered the local community (Knight, 1978).

   This has been one of the few preventive measures taken at a level in which the lay community could actively participate.

b. *Creating the first user forum* in mental health (Iris Nutting, then team leader of Camden mental health team at Friern Hospital) in the early 1980s.

   Responding to the beginning of the process of hospital closure, Ms. Nutting – literally on her own with one volunteer who did not work for social services – decided to establish this first forum. She invited some of the more articulate ex-patients of Friern, who were also members of Camden Mind, for a consultation process around the closure policy, aiming to achieve a policy recommendation document.

   The results surpassed these expectations. Not only did the users prepare the document, but many of them became involved in the management of resettlement projects in the area, and a number moved on to become leaders of the British user movement. One became a qualified social worker; another a researcher who is running a user-led research unit.

The risk taken here was that the users might not live up to the challenge, might not come on a regular basis, might not find the policy exercise useful, or might have a mental health crisis and not come back (indeed some participants had a crisis, but most of them did come back).

c. *The Chesterfield support network,* in which users run their own groups within a large community centre and are members of the centre's management committee since 1982 (Hennelly 1990).

This service enables the users to run their own activities on their own, inclusive of budget and constitution. Paid workers are available for individual consultation if needed. It is based in a generic community centre, and its users send representatives to the management committee of that centre.

The risk taken is to put to the test the Strengths approach by letting users lead their own groups, within an environment which is ordinary and not geared specifically to the needs of users with mental health problems.

Users are proud of the achievements of the network, which are theirs not less than the workers'.

d. *Residential crisis facilities* (Greenwich, 1980s, Kettering, 1990s).

These facilities were established by social services, offering both a drop-in and a respite option.

Although psychiatrists come on a sessional basis, they are not staff members. People in crisis require considerable attention, and things can go wrong in terms of harm to self and property, and less so in harm to others. Indeed, the Greenwich facility closed down after a couple of years due to the burnout of its staff group (Brangwen, 1990), while the Kettering facility is still going strong. Perhaps the differences lie in the type of support provided to the workers.

Such facilities top the users' agenda as an alternative to hospitalisation when in crisis.

e. *The Building Bridges project* (Diggins, 2000) began in the late 1990s. It offers children and parents (who have a mental illness) tailor-made support of different kinds.

This project was initiated in a south London borough by senior social workers in consultation with users and members of other professions, in response to the high number of black children going into care when their parents had a mental health crisis. It is run by a voluntary organisation with joint funding and initial Department of Health funding. The project offers casework, counselling, group work, weekends away and liaison with schools. The main feature is ensuring that each member of the family is attended to and gets the intervention method appropriate to her/his needs.

The risk taken here include child protection going wrong, parents who may harm their children, and children whose growth may be harmed by staying with the parent who has a mental illness. The project takes care of young carers, and enables parents to remain in the parenting role.

This project provides both measures of risk avoidance and risk taking, preventive and crisis response.

f. *The Family Group Conference* in mental health project as a risk taking enterprise.

The Family Group Conference follows the New Zealand Maori custom in which the community elders made joint decisions, having listened to each individual involved. Family and friends are invited to a meeting or series of meetings if need be, chaired by an independent chairperson. They are informed of the concerns raised by the professionals and the range of available options to meet these concerns. The family group decisions are to be followed by the professionals too.

In the Essex Social Services project (2002) the focus has been on an adult with serious mental health problems in Essex, and his/her family and friends. These meetings are perceived as high, but worthwhile, risk due to a three-fold baseline reasoning. When they are taking place, the family group has reached the point of "no-return", as the adult, or a child, may have to be taken out of the family, symbolising the family group's failure to look after itself and its own. It is judged that without a real shake-up no change is going to take place; the meetings can shake up and unstuck the "status quo" in which the group has been paralysed or acting in a destructive way, even though this is a high risk-taking strategy.

Negative risks may entail the following:

- Some family members have come reluctantly.
- Painful secrets may be revealed.
- The level of pain will be so high that the family group will never be able to work together again.
- The group is unable to reach a decision.
- The decision reached is beyond the menu of possibilities outlined by the professionals.
- However, if the risk taking is successful, then:
- Group members came because they care about each other.
- Good experiences will be shared too.
- The group discovers it has more strengths than it thought before the meeting.
- The group reached a decision shared by most members.
- The decision is within the menu of possibilities outlined by professionals.

It is assumed that with the shake-up that the family group conference brings about, the abilities within the family group have a much better chance of coming to the fore, even though the emotional burden has not been worked through. With an agreement, a commitment to put it into action, and a sense of ownership of the solution, as well as of being in control, there is a much better chance that things will move in the right direction.

The specific study of sixteen family group conferences demonstrates positive views of the process, and bodes well for the future, which was bleak up to the point of having the family group conference. It also highlights the fact that carers can be meaningful and equal partners to major decision-making.

g. *User researchers and risk taking*

Encouraging mental health service users and enabling them to become researchers is a risk taking strategy insofar as the following may happen:

- Users may drop out during the training due to personal crisis or disillusionment with research.

- The research work with other users may lead them to reliving painful experiences.
- They may be less good researchers than fully qualified ones, and hence carry out their research work at a lower level of quality than qualified researchers.

As against these risks stands the wish to redress the serious imbalance in our knowledge about mental ill health and mental health services, namely the fact that most of our current knowledge has not included users' perspectives, and if anything had invalidated their perspectives.

Furthermore, the perceiving of users as researchers can be contemplated only by those believing in the Strengths approach, in the ability of users to learn to the sophisticated level most research tasks require within a short time, and in the validity of users' views.

It therefore becomes a challenge – or a risk taking strategy – to develop good enough support networks and project methods to reduce the risks outlined above, while enhancing users' abilities to be good researchers (Castillo, 2002, Ramon, 2003).

## SUMMARY

Risk is an emotive issue in mental health practice, as well as for the lay public in all European societies. The emotive layer relates to the fear that the unpredictable behaviour of people experiencing mental illness will lead to physical hurt of others primarily, but also of themselves, pushing into the direction of risk avoidance.

Nevertheless, I hope a convincing case has been made in this chapter as to:

- why risk taking is inherent in mental health social work;
- why it should be focused upon and developed further;
- the fact that it can be carried out while taking into account risk avoidance issues, but without letting the latter dictate the agenda.

Social workers are better equipped than other mental health professionals to do so, as they have the initial values, the knowledge and the skills required, and a history of doing so successfully. Yet the retrenchment into risk avoidance, canonised by the role of the ASW, has meant that very little of their time and energy is spent on this necessary element of good mental health work, despite the historical legacy.

I would like to argue that it is high time to re-claim this ground, at a time when the mental health system has become more open to preventive and promoting mental health work, and at the time when the role of social workers in mental health is re-examined. As we know well, this shift would require the commitment of social workers first and foremost, as other professions are keen to claim this ground for themselves.

## References

Barnes, M./Bowl, R./Fisher, M. (1990): *Sectioned*; London: Routledge.

Beck, U. (1992): *The Risk Society*; London: Sage.

Bowers, L. (2002): *Dangerous and Severe Personality Disorder – Response and Role of the Psychiatric Team;* London: Routledge.

Brandon, D./Atherton, K./Brandon, A. (1996): *Handbook of Care Planning; London*: Positive Publications.

Brandon, D. (1997): *The Trick of Being Ordinary;* Cambridge: Anglia Polytechnic University.

Brangwyn, G. (1990): *Constructing a Crisis-Focused Social Service*; in: Ramon, S. (ed.) Psychiatry in Transition, London: Pluto Press.

Brophy, L./Campbell, J./Healy, B. (2003): Dilemmas in the Case Manager's Role – Implementing Involuntary Treatment in the Community; in: *Special Edition on Psychiatry, Psychology and Law of the Journal of the Australian and New Zealand Association of Psychiatry,* Psychology and Law.

Brown, G.W., Harris. T. (1978): *The Social Origins* of Depression; London: Tavistock Publications.

Bunce, D./West, M.A. (1996): Stress Management and Innovation Interventions at Work; in: *Human Relations*, 49, 209-232.

Campbell, J. et al (2001): The Management and Supervision of Approved Social Workers – Aspects of Law, Policy and Practice; in: *The Journal of Social Welfare and Family Law.*

Castillo, H. (2003): *Personality Disorder: Trauma or Temperament*?; London: Jessica Kingsley.

Department of Health (1999): *The National Service Framework for Mental Health*; London: HMSO.

Diggins, M. (2000): Innovation as a Professional Way of Life – the Building Bridges Project for Parents-Users of Mental Health Services and their Children; in: Ramon, S. (ed.) *A Stakeholder Approach to Innovation in Mental Health Services*, Brighton: Pavilion.

Essex Social Services Department (2002): *Essex Family Group Conference in Mental Health*, Essex County Publications.

Ferguson, H. (2001): Social Work, Individualisation and Life Politics; in: *British Journal of Social Work*, 31, 41-55.

Foster, N. (2001): Involuntary Outpatient Commitment: Managing Mental Health Risks the New Hampshire Way; in: *Journal of Mental Health and Learning Disabilities Care*, 4, 11.

Foster, N. (2002): Control, Citizenship and "Risk" in Mental Health: Perspectives from UK, US and Australia; *Paper presented at the Socrates European Conference on Risk and Mental Health*, University College Cork, May 9th 2002.

Furedi, F. (1997): *Culture of Fear: Risk-Taking and the Morality of Low Expectation*; London: Cassell.

Giddens, A. (1991): *Modernity and Self-identity*; Cambridge: Polity Press.

Healy, B./Brophy, L. (2002): Law, Psychiatry and Social Work; in: Swain, P.A. *The Shadow of the Law: The Legal Context of Social Work Practice*, New South Wales: The Federation Press.

Hennelly, R. (1990): Mental Health Resource Centres; in: Ramon, S. (ed.) *Psychiatry in Transition*; London: Pluto Press.

Hiday, V.A./Scheid-Cook, T.L. (1989): A Follow-up of Chronic Patients Committed to Outpatient Treatment; in: *Hospital and Community Psychiatry*, 40, 4, 52-58.

Home Office and the Department of Health (1999): *Managing Dangerous People with Severe Personality Disorder: Proposal for Policy Development*; London: HMSO.

Hugman, G./Pearson, G. (1995): *The Silent Partners*; London: National Schizophrenia Fellowship.

Knight, C. (178): *Neighbourhood Support Groups*; London: Family Welfare Association.

May, R./Hartley, J./Knight, T. (2003): Making the Personal Political; in the *Psychologist*, 16, 4, 182-183.

McDermott, R. (ed.) (1975): *Self Determination in Social Work*; London: Routledge and Kegan Paul.

Mental Health Media (2003): What Women Want – Mainstreaming Women's Mental Health; Mental Health Media, *www.mhmedia.com.*

Rose, N. (2000): *Powers of Freedom – Reframing Political Thought*; Cambridge: Cambridge University Press.

Ramon, S. (ed.) (1991): *Beyond Community Care – Normalisation and Integration Work*; Basingstoke: Mind Macmillan.

Ramon, S. /Savio, M. (2000): A Scandal of the 80ws and 90s – Media Representations of Mental Illness Issues in Britain and Italy; in: Ramon, S. (ed) *A Stakeholder's Approach to Innovation in Mental Health Services: A Reader for the 21st Century*, Brighton: Pavilion Publishing.

Ramon, S./Castillo, H. Morant, N. (2001): Experiencing Personality Disorder – A Participative Research; in: *International Journal of Social Psychiatry*, 41, 4, 1-15.

Ramon, S. (2003a) (ed): *Users Researching Health and Social Care – An Empowering Agenda?;* Birmingham: Venture Press.

Ramon, S. (2003b): *Evaluating Three Turning Point Projects – A Multi-stakeholder Perspective*; Unpublished Report, July.

Rapaport, J. (2003): The Ghost of the Nearest Relative under the Mental Health Act 1983 – Past, Present, and Future; in: *Journal of Mental Health Law*, 51-65.

Rapp, C.A. (1998): *The Strengths Model – Case Management with People Suffering from Severe and Persistent Mental Illness*; Oxford University Press.

Rose, N. (2000): *Powers of Freedom – Reframing Political Thought*; Cambridge: Cambridge University Press.

Saleebey, D. (ed.) (1992): *The Strengths Approach in Social Work Practice*; Longman.

Sawyer, P. (1975): The Right to Fail; in: McDermott, R. (ed.) *Self Determination in Social Work*, London: Routledge and Kegan Paul.

Schafer, T. (2003): Researching Empowerment; in: Ramon, S. (ed.) *Users Researching Health and Social Care: An Empowering Agenda*, Birmingham: Venture Press.

Shera, W./Healy, B./Aviram, U./Ramon, S. (2002): Mental Health Policy and Practice – A Multi-country Comparison; in: *Journal of Health and Mental Health Social Work*, 35, 1-2, 547-575.

Thomas, C.S./Stone, K./Osborn, M./Thomas, P./Fisher, M. (1993): Psychiatric Morbidity and Compulsory Admission among UK-Born Europeans, Afro-Caribbeans and Asians in Central Manchester; in: *British Journal of Psychiatry*, 163, 91-99.

Wainwright, T. (1992): The Changing Perspective of a Resettlement Team; in: Ramon, S. (ed.) *Psychiatric Hospital Closure – Myths and Realities*, London: Chapman Hall.

Williams, C. (2002): A *Survey of Approved Social Work Services*; Durham: Northern Centre for Mental Health.

Wolfensberger, W. (1983): The Principle of Social Role Valorisation; in: *Mental Retardation*, 21,6, 234-9.

In: Knowledge in Mental Health
Editors: L.Sapouna and P. Herrmann, pp. 57-67
ISBN 1-59454-812-9


*Chapter 4*

# The Recovery Approach: The Desired Service User Empowerment Process[1]

***Kieran Crowe and Karen Taylor***
Irish Advocacy Network, Rooskey, Co. Monaghan, Ireland.

## Abstract

In spite of growing evidence to the contrary, many people believe that when a person has been labelled with having an enduring form of mental illness they can never fully recover and most professionals believe that mental illness is a permanent condition. As long as the general framework for mental health is located within a disease based framework, mental health services and professionals will continue to provide services based on what they believe is best for the person. Social policy and care practice will continue to be misinformed, in that the needs will be those of the service system and not the person. The authors are proposing a hypothesis, "*that a person labelled as having an enduring form of mental illness falls into the category of being a person with a disease requiring long term systems maintenance in so much as the recovery process is eliminated from the choice options available to that person*".

## Introduction

The question as to whether a person labelled as having an enduring form of mental illness is based on the general assumption that enduring forms of mental illness are lifelong and that recovery is only the exception. In spite of growing evidence to the contrary, many people believe that when a person has been labelled with having an enduring form of mental illness they can never fully recover, and most professionals believe that mental illness is a permanent condition.

---

[1] Service users referred to in this chapter are either current or former users of mental health services.

Barker et al. (1998) states: "Ironically, despite his widespread infamy within the psychiatric field, Tom Szasz appears, almost single-handedly, to have driven the editors of the DSM to convert all their loose talk about mental illness into multifarious forms of psychiatric disorder. Now, fewer and fewer people can lay claim to full mental 'normality', hence the need for politicians, and economists, to concoct the cruel tautology of 'serious mental illness".

As long as the general framework for mental health is located within a disease-based framework, mental health services and professionals will continue to provide services based on what they believe is best for the person. Social policy and care practice will continue to be misinformed, in that the needs will be those of the service system and not the person.

The authors are proposing a hypothesis, "that a person labelled as having an enduring form of mental illness falls into the category of being a person with a disability requiring long-term systems maintenance insomuch as the recovery process is eliminated from the choice options available to that person". Once a recovery model is built into the process, maintenance changes to short-term support, similar to that required by someone who fractured a limb or had a viral infection, for example.

Phil Barker, Visiting Professor at Trinity College, Dublin, states: Everyone is talking recovery these days. Recovery – or at least the language of recovery – is slowly beginning to be spoken. We might well ask 'Do they really mean it?' or even, 'Do they know what they are talking about?' For the politics of mental health remain as polarised as ever, with the loud voice calling for more coercion through the proposed changes to the mental health act on one side, to the little voice of recovery-speak at the other. The middle ground remains as muddied as ever. How practitioners, far less people needing services and support, manage to reconcile these differences is beyond us (www.tidal-model.co.uk).

What is needed is a model of recovery based on the premise that anyone could be labelled mentally ill at some time or other in his or her life based on an assumption that severe emotional distress forms a part of the existential act of living. Somehow we need to make the connection along the continuum of: Severe emotional distress → Empowerment→ Recovery →Ongoing emotional healing.

Dr. Dan Fisher and his colleagues at the National Empowerment Centre, USA, propose an empowerment model of recovery based on the above where the continuum becomes a cyclical process (See diagram 1).

Dr. Fisher (http://www.power2u.org/) states:

> Unfortunately, the label and identity of a mental patient is so deep that we and the people around us continue to interpret life's normal swings of emotion as symptoms of continuing illness. After people have recovered from mental illness they still go through the emotional healing that everyone else is involved in. That is why the diagram shows that recovery is usually followed by the emotional healing.

Dr. Fisher's model clearly shows that if there are insufficient supports and coping mechanisms available to the person, there is a likelihood that the person will remain caught in a negative cycle that has often been described as the "revolving door" or most recently the "whirling door" mental health service system. Only when the person has some sense of a meaningful social role, combined with adequate supports and skills for coping and self-management, can real recovery begin to take place.

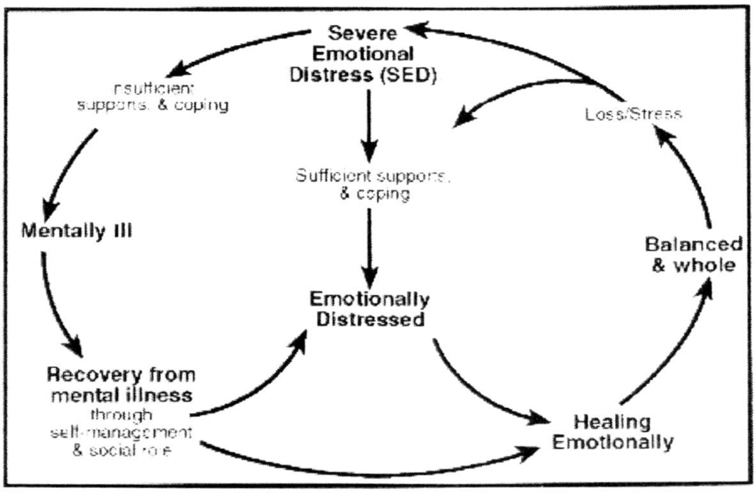


**Empowerment Model of Recovery from Mental Illness**
by Daniel B. Fisher, M.D., Ph.D. and Laurie Ahern
©1998 National Empowerment Center, Inc.

11

Diagram 1.

The movement from a disease-based framework is both a matter of personal choice and the breaking down of the systemic factors that inhibit a recovery process. Tackling these systemic factors is crucial for allowing the personal choice component of recovery to take root.

Dr. Fisher goes on to say:

> "With the *label of mental illness*, a whole new set of discriminations and problems must be overcome. There is a loss of rights. People can lose property, lose custody of children, lose privacy and lose due process before the law. They are basically taken out of the traditional legal system and placed in the extra-legal psychiatric system. The major task then in *recovering from mental illness* is to regain social roles and identities which are recognized as valid by oneself and the people in one's community. This may mean getting a job, being a volunteer, or becoming a student. It also means regaining rights, a process which the Americans with Disabilities Act of 1990 has greatly accelerated. Recovery often depends on finding someone who believes in you. That type of relationship can help a person to dream again".

## A Matter of Personal Choice

If the paradigm changes from a model of life-long illness to an acceptance of a short-term period of severe emotional distress, then a person in such distress can be considered as having a disability and should be afforded the rights and privileges afforded to someone who may have a physical or sensory disability.

Participant input and self-determination have been the bedrock principles upon which the disability movement has achieved its success. The medical model paradigm has been replaced with the more inclusive social model, ensuring that people with disabilities have more choice and control of their lives. Within the broad disability movement there has been a shift in policy in how resources are distributed, with consumers having more and more say in how resources are distributed in the context of the social priorities and processes that affect their lives. People with disabilities are demanding autonomy in deciding the social contexts of their lives and partnership in decisions regarding their medical care.

"A Strategy for Equality", 1996, declared resoundingly that self-determination forms the basis of the broader equality agenda. Unfortunately for people in severe emotional distress, such ideals are forsaken. The rights and self-determination principles for people in severe emotional distress have not been defended with the same passion. People in severe emotional distress endure constant stigma, exclusion and abuse and, were these same conditions being experienced by those driving the disability rights agenda, there would be enormous public outcry.

With the exception of people who have managed to free themselves from dehumanizing mental health services, some committed, enlightened professionals and others, routine practices such as involuntary commitment, forced drugging, segregation both in institutions and community programs, and the routine use of restraint and seclusion within psychiatric services are unquestioned. People in severe emotional distress are the only citizens who can have their liberty taken away and be institutionalized or incarcerated without being convicted of a crime. They are the only citizens who can routinely be forced to submit to medical treatments against their will.

"Lack of insight" and "non-compliance" are just two terms to justify involuntary commitment and involuntary treatment, and when people protest against treatments they do not want, they are forced to accept regardless, on the deluded basis that they are too ill to recognise their need for treatment. Most users of psychiatric services over time will desist from overtly protesting against these enforced treatments because to do so entails heavier doses of psychotropic medication; *ipso facto*, compliance is brought about by breaking the person's will or medicating resistance. The result of this methodology is learned helplessness or internalised oppression, which is incompatible with hope and with any possibility of recovery.

## A History of Recovery

Dr. Abraham Low, an American psychiatrist, developed a Recovery Approach at the end of the 1930s, having noticed the need for support mechanisms for patients who were discharged from the hospital. He envisaged the formation of self-help groups of ex-patients and established an organisation known as Recovery Incorporated, which still exists today. Dr. Loren Mosher developed Soteria House in California which ran from 1971-1983. Soteria means 'salvation' or 'deliverance'. It offered another way to realise recovery, through supported everyday living. Current key figures in the US Recovery Movement include Dr. Dan Fisher and Pat Deegan.

In Europe, the main development was the anti-psychiatry movement associated with Dr. R. D. Laing. Dr. Luc Ciompi developed 'Soteria Berne' in Switzerland. He demonstrated that people with serious forms of mental illness – e.g. schizophrenia – could recover in less than 3 months, using the Soteria model. The Soteria projects in the USA and Switzerland – and Professor Yrjo Alanen's similar project in Finland – showed that medication was often unnecessary. Dr. Joseph Berke has run the "Arbours" in London for 35 years – offering a psychosocial environment for people with serious forms of mental illness. In the 1980s Marius Romme, a Dutch psychiatrist and Sandra Escher, a journalist, started to organise conferences for voice hearers. This led on to research with "voice hearers" and conferences in the UK, and this in turn led to the development of the National Hearing Voices Network. The Network has a been a self-help group for many users, including Paddy McGowan, who has become a key figure in the Recovery Movement in Ireland, North and South.

## Contrasting Approaches

It is helpful to contrast a disease-based maintenance approach, which has dominated psychiatry over the years, with the emerging recovery-based approach, which contextualises recovery within a social and psychological framework rather than a purely medical framework.

### The Disease-Based Maintenance Approach

A disease-based maintenance approach functions in an environment where the culture is dominated by very low expectations of users. It assumes that users will need services indefinitely and that all the inter-disciplines are an extension of the medically-orientated service system. The focus of staff is on observation and they are trained and encouraged to note the slightest negative changes in clients which then require higher doses of medication. People are discouraged from taking risks on the grounds that failure is likely to give rise to further episodes. Risk taking in an environment of support helps a person grow in self-confidence and indeed self-knowledge. In the mainstream service environment there is no formal process to encourage service users to move on, and a culture of dependence is maintained. The service itself becomes so crisis-orientated that only those assessed as needing the service most get access to it. The mushroom effect is that as more and more people are in a state of dependence on the services, a bottomless pit is created, sucking in any available resources.

### The Recovery-Based Approach

The recovery-based approach aims to increase interdependence and autonomy. People are encouraged and supported to maintain their social roles and make informed choices in relations to these roles. The service is geared specifically with the intention of and commitment to assisting them to maintain their social roles insofar as they themselves have the capacity to do so. In fact the role itself is determined by this capacity, not as something externally constructed but constructed by the person him/herself. Peer support and peer advocacy assist the people to identify, articulate and meet their own needs.

Curtis (1997) defines recovery as "a process, not a place. It is about recovering what was lost: rights, roles, responsibilities, decisions, potential and support. It is not about symptom elimination, but about what an individual wants, how s/he can get there, and how others can help/support them to get there. It is about rekindling hope for a productive present and a rewarding future – and believing that one deserves it. Recovery involves people having a personal vision of the life they want to live, seeing and changing patterns, discovering how symptoms can be managed and doing it, finding new ways and reasons, doing more of what works and less of what doesn't. Recovery is about reclaiming the roles of a "healthy" person, rather than a "sick" person. Recovery is about getting there."

It is important to note, though, that there is no specific template for recovery in a person's life, as the journey is defined by the individual concerned. However, research does indicate that there are common themes in recovery stories. The user and the practitioner alike must believe that life can be different; there must be a sense of hope in and for people. Once hope has been engendered, people start taking personal responsibility for their lives and managing their well-being. This builds a sense of personal control and self-determination and for some this is a process of baby steps at first, but in the context of a person who has never had autonomy or has learned through time to become helpless and dependent, this is understandable.

| Value/ Assistance | Disease-based maintenance | Recovery-based approach |
|---|---|---|
| **Could anyone become mentally ill?** | NO: There is a genetic predisposition | YES: Therefore we are all equally human |
| **Cause of mental illness** | Permanent brain disorder | Severe emotional distress and loss of social role |
| **Recovery** | Lifelong process | Complete recovery possible |
| **Goal of help** | Maintenance | Full recovery |
| **Control** | Coercion by team; external control | Person-centered, voluntary; control by self |
| **Pace** | Set by team | Set by individuals themselves |
| **Relationships** | Professional distance | Peer connections |
| **Primary assistance** | Medication | Person who believes in you |
| **Main social setting** | Professionally-run | Peer-run |
| **Rights** | Violated often | Respected |
| **Outcome** | Dependency; lackingResponsibility | Self-management; gain sense of responsibility |
| **Choice of help** | Case manager | Full choice; consumer-run, psychosocial, therapy |
| **Primary person** | Little choice and narrowly Medical | Personal assistant |
| **Housing and money** | Compliance with services Required | Compliance with services not required |
| **Function of medication** | Required for lifelong Maintenance | Used as a tool, by choice |

Diagram 2.

Service users need to find empowerment from within and this is gained through locating their "real self" or their 'voice' again. This can be quite challenging for mental health professionals to deal with and can be viewed as non-compliance. Peer-advocacy provides support and opportunity for people to re-engage with their own environment; to experiment, try, succeed and fail, and the goal of peer advocacy is toward Self-advocacy. The peer support of someone who had similar though unique experiences themselves is indispensable, and it is extremely difficult for recovery to take place without the support of someone who truly knows that things can improve and that there is hope even in the depths of despair.

Hope evolves from restoring meaning to life, and this is where recovery can become a sort of spiritual pilgrimage. What is meant here by spiritual is the meaning a person derives from an internal set of values and/or beliefs. We will discuss later in the chapter how the person's narrative becomes the fulcrum from which this sense of meaning takes root and grows. Personal meaning helps to develop a sense of identity. The opportunity to be able to place one's stamp of uniqueness and individuality on the environment is crucial to recovery.

In Diagram 2, Fisher et al (1998) outlines the values and assistances needed comparing a Disease-based maintenance approach viz. a Recovery-based approach.

Recovery is a journey that is unique to every individual. Consequently it is better thought of as an 'approach' rather than as a formal 'model' though, as will be explained later in the chapter, an approach that must be located in a congruent environmental model. It is an inclusive and a pragmatic approach. It recognises that different people will find different routes. Treatments and interventions provided by the medical, social, psychological and other practitioners may be useful on *their* journey. It is, however, the person who exercises choices over these matters in the context of rights and responsibilities.

## Recovery is Better Seen as an Amalgamation of Processes Rather than a Model

There is no template for recovery; it a not a goal achieved along linear definitions. It is a unique journey filled with uncertainty but there are some underlying components crucial to the process. The recovery environment is the most critical of these components. Often, those who make a significant difference are those who have been users of services themselves, but who have been on their own journey of recovery. They can be positive role models who share their lived experiences and they can offer authentic hope. What is important, though, is that users who are in recovery have done some work themselves and have a developed awareness, particularly in relation to their own needs. The recovery-based approach is not proscriptive in that the resources and power to change one's environment are located within the person him/herself. Diversity and difference are valued in such environments and inclusiveness is a basic tenet.

Russinova (1999) identifies the following as the interpersonal resources vital to assisting the recovery process:

- Belief in the person's potential and strength
- Value for the person as a unique human being
- Accepting the person for who they are

- Listening non-judgmentally
- Tolerance for uncertainty about the future of the person
- Acceptance of the person's times of unwellness and failures as part of the recovery process
- Tolerance of the person's challenges and defeats
- Trusting the authenticity of the person's experiences
- Expression of genuine concern for the person's well-being
- Appropriate use of humour

## Defining a Recovery Framework

A recovery approach is important for people who use services, their carers, families and friends, since it offers some realistic measure of hope. Recovery is important to people who use services, because it is an approach that has been appropriated by service users. But a recovery framework has currency only insofar as the approach is located within a philosophical ethos which underpins the value of the person's narrative within the overall context.

Traditional assumption offers a template for normalcy to which people either belong to or deviate from. Traditional approaches adhere to modernist assumptions such that objectivity is assumed; there is a singular truth and if we search diligently, we can discover it. This approach is based on "scientific" essences and structures; experts discover "facts" and prescribe corrective measures; if the person does not agree with these, s/he is considered as in denial or being resistant.

Solution-focused approaches, although post-modernist; focus on competencies, resources and strengths as a means of overcoming difficulties and asserting the positive. Both approaches are limited in that they operate from a position of certainty, and thus are representative of an either/or perspective in that they tend to leave out the rest of the picture.

Post-modernism is rooted in the view that there are no facts, only "interpretations," that each perspective originates from the workings of the "will to power." Solution-focused approaches, while adhering to post-modernist assumptions, address and focus on the competencies and strengths of the person, replacing the deficit story with one of success. In this model, active participation in the solution by the client is required as the more positive aspects of the person's ability are highlighted, thus relegating trauma and problems to the background.

Generally, questions that flow from certainty assumptions have "right or wrong" answers related to socially accepted norms, and are designed more to validate collective thoughts and premises than to uncover the person's definition of the situation. Structural theorists fit people into what they consider a normative template in an attempt to replicate healthy structural functioning.

Social constructionism is rooted in social interpretation and the influences of language, family, and culture. Social construction theory proposes that there is an evolving set of meanings that continually emerge from social interactions. These meanings are part of a general flow of constantly changing narratives. By this they mean that the ways in which our meanings are constructed are often invisible to us, as are the elements which compose it. In western society, modernist ideas about the nature of reality stem mainly from nineteenth-century Descartesian-Newtonian mechanistic and reductionistic perspectives.

Children are born without culture; education is the process of enculturation which supplies them with the canopy woven by the particular milieu into which they happen to be born. The social world we are born into is experienced by the child as the sole reality; the rules of this world are non-problematic. They require no explanation, and they are neither challenged nor doubted. Through socialization, the socially constructed meanings are internalized; they are filtered and understood through meaningful symbols. From these socially constructed meanings flow psychological meanings and scripts for behaviour.

We co-construct a consensus reality through language with another in a continual interaction with the socio-cultural environment. Thus, what is "real" is that which is co-constructed through language and interaction by persons in continual interplay with the surrounding socio-cultural environment. People create an image of their world by noticing behaviour in others that confirms their own identities and definitions of situations and by selectively ignoring nonconsensual attitudes and behaviour.

## The Narrative

Using the above as a background for proposing a social constructionist narrative model for recovery, the issues can be divided into three different sections of one story:

Section 1: The person's narrative about their individual past, families of origin including the broader family myth, e.g. heroines, heroes and villains.
Section 2: The narrative about their present relationships.
Section 3: The narrative about what they see for their future.

An individual's reality/narrative is maintained by developing a personal sense of self that is emerging from the larger socio-cultural stories. From earliest interactions and ongoing socialization, individuals construct a reality around meanings which includes a preferred, though not always conscious way of relating to others. This then becomes the basis for how they view others and how they expect others to view them. In many ways, these perceptual preferences determine predictable ways of interacting with others, either positive or negative or both. The narrative of the past can be revised holistically in two ways. Firstly, the socio-cultural context can be re-framed. An example of this could be a person born into a particular community where rage is used to justify socio-political ideals through violence. Secondly, the personal context can also be re-framed, e.g. a person who defends a parent's brutality on the basis that they deserved to be beaten.

When uncovering the stories about the present, it is useful to examine information the person selects from their environment and how they fit that information into an already existing meaning system so as to reinforce that system. In so doing, they also learn the other side of the picture, what they are *not* selecting out of the environment and especially the "shadow" aspects. The "shadow" here refers to the term coined by the psychiatrist/psychotherapist Carl Jung. The "shadow" refers to the unconscious aspects of both individual and collective personality that are unwelcome and generally do not fit with the prevailing identity of either the individual or group. "*The shadow personifies everything that the person refuses to acknowledge about himself ... – for instance inferior character traits and other incompatible tendencies*" Jung (1971). For example, a person who carries the stigma associated with having a psychiatric diagnosis can actually construct their experience of having a breakdown in terms of having a breakthrough.

When it is accepted that a person's meaning systems are socially constructed, it then becomes possible to deconstruct them. The processes by which the person's meaning systems can be uncovered and then expanded in order to "make room" for new experiences are revealed. Then the possibility of choice arises in terms of whether they want to keep the uncovered meaning system or to change/expand it.

Once notions of meaning systems are accepted by the person, and the broader meaning systems are uncovered, competing meaning systems become obvious. It is not apparent to most individuals that there are alternative ways of behaving at each stage of the life cycle. Our meaning systems make areas outside the dominant ones appear invisible. This invisibility serves to maintain and foster adherence to the dominant definitions. In fact, the function of socialization and of the sanctions against moving outside the dominant scripts is to keep individuals within it. To find, name, focus on, and help the person experience alternative meanings and how "shadow projections" operate will often be the start of a reconstruction process that makes the recovery of a positive social role possible.

The views expressed in this chapter are that change is always occurring and we have a choice in change. Our knowledge about how to behave is learned by social definitions of appropriate and inappropriate ways of behaving; however, we can choose to develop our own personal attitudes and concepts which differ from the traditional ones. Change requires at least a two-sided perspective.

Now, a whole range of meaning systems are available to the person and what once was invisible holds potential for new solutions. The original meaning system which held the problem has been deconstructed and expanded to include new descriptions. The person can now begin to focus on the future.

This expansion of the meaning system is essential for the future narrative construction, which includes a range of new possibilities. These new narratives contain new attitudes and behaviours that are truly authentic because they are created from the person's inner resources. Thus, the recovery environment is one where it is safe to test and develop these new attitudes and behaviours in the context of exploring the implications of the meanings that ensue. In so doing, the person's total narrative past, present and future opens up, and this includes the "shadow". Inner strengths and resources evolve, and creativity flourishes as the person attempts to articulate this new sense of self, abundant with psychological meaning.

## SUMMARY

Traditional models of recovery are based on a position of certainty in that there is a model of normality that if the person adheres to, they will be deemed normal and recovered. Non-adherence is caused by a bio-, psycho- or social pathology. Solution-focused therapy, although believing in post-modernist assumptions, in many ways relies on the certainty principle in that there is a focus on the competencies, resources, and strengths to the exclusion in some cases of the reason why the person entered the service in the first place. The Social

Constructionist Recovery Approach presented in this chapter, based on a post-modernist stance, assists users in expanding, rather than replacing, their view. This perceptual expansion occurs through a both/and position and through changes in the narratives that users hold about their meaning systems. This approach, while incorporating many different aspects of social constructionist theory, integrates and presents an approach focusing on helping users to reconstruct what is important to them, in order to provide them with more options, more choices and more hope.

## References

Ahern, L./Fisher, D. (1999): People Can and Do Recover from Mental Illness; in: *NEC Newsletter*, Lawrence, MA.

Anthony, W.A. (1993): Recovery from Mental Illness: The Guiding Vision of The Mental Health Service System in the 1990s; in: *Psychosocial Rehabilitation Journal.*

Barker P./Keady J./Croom S./Stevenson C./Adams T./Reynolds B. (1998): The Concept of Serious Mental Illness: Modern Myths and Grim Realities; in: *Journal of Psychiatric and Mental Health Nursing* 5(4) 247-54.

Barker P./Buchanan P., *www.tidal-model.co.uk/New%20Colonisation.htm*

Berger, P./Luckman, T. (1966): The Social Construction of Reality; New York: Irvington.

Commission on the Status of People with Disabilities (1996): *A Strategy for Equality;* Dublin: Stationary Office.

Curtis, L. (1997): *New Directions: International Overview of Best Practices in Recovery and Rehabilitation Services for People with Serious Mental Illness*; University of Vermont, USA: Center for Community Change.

De Shazer, S. (1991): *Putting Difference to Work*; New York: W.W. Norton & Company.

Faulkner, Alison, et al. (2000): *Strategies for Living: A Report Of User-Led Research into People's Strategies for Living with Mental Distress*; London: The Mental Health Foundation.

Fisher, D./Deegan, P. (1998): *Final Report on Recovery Project*; Rockville, MD: Center for Mental Health Services.

Jung, Carl G. (1971): *The Collected Works*; vol. 9, Aion, London: Routledge.

Ralph, R.O./Lambric, T.M./Steele, R.B. (1996): Recovery Issues in a Consumer Developed Evaluation of the Mental Health System; *Presentation at 6th Annual Mental Health Services Research and Evaluation Conference*, Arlington, VA, February, pp.1-13.

Reeves A., (2000): *Recovery, a Holistic Approach*; Handsell Publishing.

Wallcraft, J./Read, J./Sweeney, A. (2003): *On Our Own Terms, Users and Survivors of Mental Health Services Working Together for Support and Change*; London: The Sainsbury Centre for Mental Health.

In: Knowledge in Mental Health
Editors: L.Sapouna and P. Herrmann, pp. 69-83
ISBN 1-59454-812-9


*Chapter 5*

# MENTAL HEALTH ASSISTANCE IN ITALY: THE TORINO REHABILITATION PROGRAM*

***Caterina G. Corbascio Fox***
Turin Mental Health Services;
Department Psychology University of Turin, Italy

## ABSTRACT

This chapter is focused on the work of a psychiatric rehabilitation centre in Turin Italy. Recent trends in neo-institutionalisation of people affected by severe mental illness have become an actual threat in Italy that may destroy the achievements of the 18O Law, the Basaglia Law. The closure of psychiatric hospitals in Italy has been the basis for creating innovative services in the community with the aim of taking care of people with severe mental illness without segregating them in renewed psychiatric institutions. For this aim we have adopted distinct principles in order to be able to provide effective and adequate care for these patients. Chronicity is considered a result of scientific and/or organizational inadequacy of treatments. Our project has also worked with users self-help associations for promoting patients' re-acquisition of civil rights and social integration.

## INTRODUCTION: THE ITALIAN MENTAL HEALTH REFORM

Re-institutionalization of patients with severe mental illnesses has become an actual threat: if successful it may hamper the results achieved by the application in Italy of Law 180

* This work was partially supported by grants from Psichiatria Democratica (Napoli, Italy) and from Fondazione CRT (Torino, Italy)

(On Voluntary and Compulsory Health Treatments), better known as the Basaglia Act, which is considered one of the most innovative and courageous interventions in the psychiatric field.

In the sixties, mental health care in Italy was essentially based on psychiatric hospitals, which were in those days called "asylums", as dictated by the first reference Law issued in 1904.

Dismantling psychiatric hospitals formally began with Law 180, issued in May 1978. The Law considered compulsory treatment only as an exceptional measure, which led to the development of a Community Mental Health Centres network all over the country for providing alternative ways to deal with mentally disabled people within the community.

In fact, the de-institutionalization process had begun years before 1978 in the Italian psychiatric hospitals directed by Franco Basaglia, namely Trieste, Gorizia and Arezzo. The experience gathered in these different hospitals showed that:

i) psychiatric wards could function in an open manner and
ii) a non-repressive organization – even if inside the institution – may yield highly positive results (see, Pirella, 1999). The last inference was that
iii) it was possible to close psychiatric hospitals and to treat people with mental health problems in the community. Immediate practical consequences were a reduction in both compulsory treatments and patients' tendency to clinical regression.

Basaglia's "open door" approach dramatically changed patients' feelings and relationships with the external environment and with those in direct charge of their care. In other words, the long-term in-patient began to "discover his right to live a human life" (Basaglia, 1968).

## THE ITALIAN POLITICAL AND SOCIAL CONTEXT

A critical factor in the early sixties for the development of the new Law was the presence of widespread reforming movements all over the country led by university students, the working class, the trade unions, and leftist and radical parties. This unique social *milieu* led to the approval of innovative legislative projects which included legislation on divorce, abortion, rights for workers and lastly, Law 180.

Franco Basaglia was the principal proponent of Law 180, which went beyond the issues of mental health. Leftist and the radical parties, along with a broad-based support by ordinary people, were the supporters for Basaglia's action, which led to the approval of the reforming law by the Italian parliament in May 1978. Law 180 was included in the new National Health Service Act, which defined the catchment areas for all health services and a uniform system of budget allocation, not discriminating against psychiatric services, which to this day remain part of the national health system.

Basaglia and his followers considered psychiatry as the provider of scientific support for social control to the existing establishment. The resulting standards of normality and deviance produced *de facto* repressive views of discrete social groups. This approach was clearly non-medical and pointed out the role of mental institutions in the control and medicalization of social problems and deviant behaviors.

The work of Basaglia in the *manicomio (mental asylum)* of Gorizia, initially based on Maxwell Jones' ideas on therapeutic community, led to the conclusion that the core of the problem was the institution itself, where the rigid organization, control mechanisms and inflexible rules finally led to de-personalization and eradication of human dignity. The work initially promoted by Basaglia was centred on dismantling the mental institution, trying to physically eliminate the traditional barriers between people and mental patients and, at the same time, promoting community-based services necessary for living outside the hospital. The real action originated inside the hospital by abolishing the barriers between staff and patients: the hallmark of the initiative was the elimination of staff uniforms and use of keys. The result was an open-door hospital, freely accessible from outside. It was difficult for the general population and the media to understand and accept this process: this prompted the need to enlist public support, which was achieved by attracting the attention of the more open-minded politicians, who were at that time dominantly leftist in orientation. Discussions were intense, passionate and difficult, mostly with professionals and Unions. Finally, the liberation of mental patients became an official position of the Italian Communist Party which in those years (the early 1970s), was reacquiring political and economical power. The difficult relationship between innovation in psychiatry and the Unions was smoothed over by the major leftist-wing parties accepting a linkage between innovation in medicine, science and psychiatry and the health conditions that the working class were facing daily in and outside the factories (Scarpa, 1974 in *La pratica della follia*, Gorizia, June 22-23, 1974). While working for the phasing-out of different state psychiatric hospitals in Arezzo, Parma and Reggio Emilia, Basaglia and his group promoted the creation of *Psichiatria Democratica* (Democratic Psychiatry), (*La pratica della follia, Gorizia, June 22, 1974, First Congress of Psichiatria Democratica*). The objectives of the association were (and still are) to pool together professional energies and initiatives in any part of society which are aimed at closing psychiatric institutions and restoring the rights of mental health patients.

## Basaglia and Law 180

The main provisions of Law 180 were the following:

1) Psychiatric assistance was to be shifted away from psychiatric hospitals to Community Mental Health Centres, newly organized in a departmental or sectorised manner to assure connections and integrations with services and community resources.
2) Admission of new patients to the existing psychiatric hospitals was not to be allowed. The building of new psychiatric hospitals was also prohibited.
3) Psychiatric wards were to be opened inside General Hospitals with a limited number of beds (no more than 14-16).
4) Compulsory treatments were to be exceptional interventions performed only when the treatment outside of the hospital was not accepted by the patient and when at the same time adequate community facilities could not be accessed.

Basaglia's action, initially considered as a technical intervention in medicine, stemmed from an analysis of the repressive role of psychiatry in society. This analysis raised several political and social issues which deeply influenced medicine. Indeed, Law 180 was the cross-point where medical, political and social issues converged. Consequently, it can be seen as the starting point for an almost revolutionary law (at least, for the country), i.e. the new National Health Service Act, issued in the same year and with far-reaching impacts on the Italian society in general.

Indeed, psychiatric hospitals were dismantled in a context of peculiar social and political events, with experiences radiating into different fields of the social and health system (e.g. care for the elderly and physically disabled people and children). The underlying principle of the Italian National Health System was that every kind of disease and disability should be cared for without segregating the patient from his normal context (home, work, leisure or activities). This aim was implemented essentially by abolishing segregation practices, while creating outpatient services featuring multi-functional flexibilities. The project was realized by deeply modifying the working style of health care operators and with the active participation of patients, families, psychiatric nurses, students and workers, psychiatrists, psychologists, journalists and local public administrators to the new assistance programs.

## Application and Implementation of Law 180

The law has been applied at different speed throughout country, essentially because each Region has its local political government, with the power to influence local health and social policies. The consequence was (and still is) the existence of standards of different quality services delivered to patients depending on where they live.

Indeed, the process of application of the Law was complicated by the need to act contemporaneously on two fronts: on the one hand, the gradual phasing out of mental hospitals and the opening of psychiatric wards in the general hospitals, and on the other the creation of the new Community Mental Health Centres in the community. The situation in some Regions was paradoxical: the opening of the new psychiatric wards in general hospitals was not complemented by the development of new services in the community due to the lack of political will. Closure of the psychiatric hospitals also brought about the necessity of "rehabilitation", or to use another expression, de-institutionalization, of the personnel (both staff and MDs) of mental hospitals, who were reluctant to accept the changes imposed by working in the Community Mental Health Centres. For these reasons there was a long delay in opening the Community Mental Health Centres, especially in southern Italy, because of the slow pace of the hospital closure process.

Needless to say, Law 180 encountered severe opposition from most of the academic psychiatrists and psychologists. They advocated that mental patients should be cared for only in clinics or hospitals, disregarding in this way all the positive results brought about by the experiments conducted by Basaglia and his followers.

Moreover, a total application of the principles inspiring Law 180 required a radical change in the clinical approach to mental patients, which has not yet been completely accepted by the psychiatric establishment, especially in the University Medical Schools which to this day remain largely dependent on biological and somatic approaches. As a tradition, universities have not been involved in delivering services to all mental patients but have always acted as "private clinics" selecting patients for admission. With a few exceptions, this has resulted in academic psychiatry remaining far removed from Community Care psychiatry, from the intended innovations of the reforming Law 180 and from the reality of local policies. Moreover, academic psychiatry remains culturally distant from the real-life problems of the people whom they should be taking care of. Indeed, the professional education of the new generation of psychiatrists, nurses and operators is now, more than 20 years after the issuing of the Law, still incomplete, lacking specific anti-institutional experience through direct involvement in psychiatric hospital closure.

This complex changing situation generated criticisms of the Law, not only by mental health professionals reluctant to change their working style, but also by patients' families' associations concerned about the destiny of their relatives in the absence of psychiatric hospitals and, in the first years of the application of the Law, in some situations, worried about the lack of adequate and dependable community-based programs.

Today, mainly for political reasons, different groups (psychiatrists, legislators and family associations among others) are pursuing strategies for the reconstitution of the old system by proposing a new law for mental health care aimed at replacing the inspiring principles of Basaglia's Law. For this reason, the country is now facing a clear dichotomy in this field, with the Parliament considering the possibility of a return to conservative psychiatry, and the majority of Italian psychiatrists having finally accepted the innovative features of Law 180.

Recent budget cuts in public health dictated by political and economic priorities have encouraged decisions with a short-term orientation such as cutting personnel costs and reducing patients' subsidies with apparently positive immediate fall-outs but detrimental in middle and long terms. These changes resulted, in the medium and long term, in the necessity of implementing residential programs, as severely disabled patients are no longer able to live independently in the community in the absence of adequate assistance and economical support. As a consequence there is a shift of state budget from public community-based services to residential programs that are mainly privately and profit driven. For these reasons it is even more important to demonstrate the effectiveness of community-based treatments in order to be able to influence budget flow.

## SECTORAL ORGANISATION OF PSYCHIATRIC CARE

Law 180 introduced for the first time in Italy the sectoral organization of psychiatric care, i.e. the Mental Health Department, where Community Mental Health Centres were to be the hinge and the main vehicle for the reform act.

The ideal strategy for the Mental Health Department would be to design personalized patient-oriented programs rather than being guided by rigid protocols, giving preference to home-based options instead of residential programs, in order to avoid new ways of segregation. This would mean to put in practice the right of the patients to live in their own homes, regardless of the diagnosis.

Another feature marking the ideal department is prioritising early interventions for patients. Early actions should be performed to prevent clinically severe regressive situations due to neglect and lack of specific intervention. Early interventions and actions should involve related services (e.g. social services, agencies for elderly people etc.) and all other resources present in the community for the promotion of social inclusion and the reduction of the need for new institutional and residential solutions.

However, the most important issue to be considered in planning a Mental Health Department is the attention to patients' quality of life, looking beyond traditional clinical outcomes. Improvement in the quality of life links clinical results (e.g. symptom reduction, recovery promotion and relapse prevention) to ethical goals (e.g. the right to access personalized care programs) and also to the benefits for society such as reduction of family burden and long-term social costs of mental illness.

It is well known that poverty and social inequality, even in industrialised countries, exacerbate problems and exclusion processes. The World Health Report for Mental Health for the year 2001 points out the existence of a "vicious circle" between poverty (unemployment, economical deprivation, low level of education), mental disturbances (higher prevalence, lack of care, negative outcomes) and economical impact (job loss, reduced productivity, increase in health expenses) (World Health Report 2001 – Mental Health: New Understanding, New Hope, WHO, Geneva, Switzerland, 2001). More than 20 years ago Basaglia had identified a direct and reciprocal link between poverty and mental disease. Moreover, economic development that generates new social imbalances will be reflected at individual levels by an increased burden of private suffering (Mezzina, 2003).

An ideal Mental Health Department must also be flexible and capable of working in a context which is continuously responding to changes of social and political systems, and strong enough to link structures in order to develop diverse programs tailored to patient needs. Another key feature is the ability to promote patients' potential for self-management and participation in community life.

Discussing treatment and future projects with patients is a simple and basic strategy to ensure their committed involvement in individual therapeutic and rehabilitation projects. The final aim is to invest power in the patients, a core principle and the most important tool used for psychiatric rehabilitation in the hospital closure programs.

Other related services (social districts, primary care, etc.) should interact with Mental Health Departments to delineate individualized and integrated projects and not merely treatment plans. Influencing related services by the de-institutionalization experience is important for avoiding segregating practices in those fields.

No less importantly, the Department should be organized on a 24-hour basis, with the aim of overcoming and preventing long -term stay in psychiatric wards by activating alternative pathways to short and long-term hospitalization.

Besides having simplified rules and guidelines, the ideal Mental Health Department should be endowed with an ethical, cultural and political background which encompasses humanity, clinical practice and science. In my view, these are the prime and essential elements in achieving a structure which will respond to the basic needs of a suffering section of the population.

## Current Obstacles

In conclusion, the current situation in Italy is that Community Mental Health Centres i.e. Community Care, are still not working as expected. In spite of high monetary and social costs and political efforts invested during the last 25 years, Community Mental Health Centres are inadequate in providing effective care, especially for severe psychiatric patients.

The reason for such negative outcome may be summarized as follows:

1) Limited flexibility and adaptability by the staff.
2) Lack of specific attention to key needs of the patients, e.g. financial assistance and housing programs.
3) Lack of a 24-hour organization for emergency intervention in the community and for home support for severe mental patients.

The consequence is that only a small number of patients is supported, namely those who are able to meet appointments and to take a job with an income and achieve financial independence, allowing them to care for themselves and their houses without institutional support.

Patients lacking such optimal features are at high risk of becoming clinically chronic, a phenomenon described as "revolving door policy", indicating repeated hospitalizations due to poor adaptation to community life in the absence of specific preventive psychiatric care.

The inadequacy of Community Mental Health Centres organisation and activities, together with the inability to respond to the housing needs of severe mental patients, generated an uncertainty which has resulted in a return to old clinical approaches and re-institutionalization of psychiatric patients.

To counteract the present trend, the Torino Rehabilitation Program has issued a general strategy based on guidelines and practical tactics, designed to be adopted by all the Community Mental Health Centres of the sector.

## Background Experience of the Torino (Turin) Rehabilitation Program

The closure of psychiatric hospitals originated in Piedmont before Law 180: the Law led to a significant decrease of the number of patients from 4,473 in 1970 to 514 in 1984 (Pirella, 1987). The experience of the Torino area was mainly through the transfer of patients to the so-called "guest communities" organized inside the buildings or areas of the former psychiatric hospitals. These early communities were organized for patient rehabilitation with the aim of further integration outside the hospital.

The Hospital Closure Program was a multi-step project, which included: i) the development of the guest communities ii) support for patients' relocation into public apartments iii) assistance in looking for appropriate job positions and iv) therapeutic support for the former patients leaving the hospital.

Our experience stems from the actions implemented for the closure of the psychiatric hospitals and represents the underlying model for our action to support patients in their homes (Corbascio, 1994; Carrucciu, et al., 1995).

Its hallmark is the adoption of projects designed *ad personam*, in order to match the needs of patients living outside of the hospital even after decades of institutionalization.

Key points of our strategy were:

1) the construction and re-construction of patients' life stories not as clinical case reports.
2) the restitution of people's identity and civil rights.
3) an entitlement and practical recognition of these rights, i.e. the power to choose, to manage personal finances and belongings, to have a house and inter-personal relationships.

In this way, patients became the real protagonists of the hospital closure: they were no more clinical cases but people with problems and desires – and choices.

The experience of those years showed that a re-acquisition of the capacity to desire (and consequently to make requests) is one of the first and reliable indicators of clinical improvement.

This way of treating psychiatric patients originated in weekly team meetings in which all the staff members participated, reconsidering the life stories of the people under our care. In our experience this approach represented a watershed, bringing immediate relevant changes. Those days were memorable for patients whose characters had been moulded by internments ranging from 20 to 50 years in length. Those situations were extreme, but even nowadays it is not unusual to take care of young patients who have already spent 10 years in so-called therapeutic communities.

Life stories helped to evoke in our minds a new representation that was the premise of a new way of interacting with patients.

Positive interactions with people with psychiatric problems require a disposition to listen, an ability to share difficulties and emotions, and specific attention to patients' point of view and desires. Our experience indicates that interactions between patients and non-professional operators yield very positive results. This is a consequence of a non-stigmatising relationship that positively influences clinical and social outcomes.

Elaboration and re-construction of life stories has been the tool for creating a new mental representation as a premise for giving back identities to the individual patients. Re-construction of identity is an important process because it restores the possibility for the individual to make plans for a reasonable future, stemming from personal desires. Schematically, the step of the process may be summarized in:

i) reacquisition of desires followed by
ii) the ability to make provisions, which ends in
iii) enabling people to take decisions (Corbascio, 2003).

Long-term patients living in residential programs develop characteristics similar to those who have spent several years in psychiatric hospitals: in the same way, they also need to reacquire the capacity to make plans and acquire control over decision-making processes.

## CURRENT ORGANISATION OF THE REHABILITATION PROGRAM

The Torino Rehabilitation Program is a specialized service belonging to one of the four Torino Mental Health Departments. Each Department covers an area of 250,000 inhabitants.

Today, the Program supports 95 patients living in 65 independent apartments: the patient sample includes 20 former guests of the psychiatric hospitals of the Torino area, as well as a group of so-called young people with chronic disease, whom the Community Mental Health Centres are unable to keep in independent living.

The working organization of the program is based on the provision of flexible outside support at a patient's house; during the day (i.e. from 8 a.m. to 8 p.m.), there are 2 teams of 10 operators (nurses and educators) moving from the service headquarters to the patients' houses, as scheduled during the weekly meeting. An operator is present at weekends for leisure activities and a nurse is on call for night and day emergencies.

The staff teams are multi-disciplinary, including a psychiatrist working in close proximity with nurses and operators of the social cooperatives.[1] (In the case of the Rehabilitation Program, the role of type A cooperatives has been to provide a different type of staff, such as educators, to work in partnership with the public health system. This can lead to an interchange of knowledge and cultural backgrounds when assistance is provided to patients by different kinds of staff with different educational backgrounds. The public services mainly use nurses for assisting patients. The type B cooperatives have had a fundamental role, especially at the beginning of the hospital closure process, because they restored patients' rights to work and to be paid as any other worker, which was very different from the exploitation of patients who were workers inside the institutions. In the 1980s there was no distinction between A and B cooperatives. This led to very advanced experiences where psychiatric patients were working together with 'normal' people and were members of the cooperative the same as the other members). The staff also includes a full-time case manager.

The program is organized through daily morning and weekly meetings: the work of the operators is based on a weekly program, leaving some extra-time for emergency interventions. Meetings with both patients and staff members are scheduled on special topics of general relevance (for example money management, problems with the house, with the other patients living there, or with neighbours). Such programs and activities are developed in close collaboration with *Arcobaleno* (Rainbow), a service users' association originating from the model of the old Primavera '85 of the Grugliasco Psychiatric Hospital.

The first step of the program's activities is the analysis of available resources and needs of patients, mainly identified as a response to their needs for a house and support.

The main asset of the program is the availability of a number of apartments, which are proof of the work done over the years to provide the Department with the necessary housing resources to meet the patients' needs. Such privileged access is extremely helpful in acute situations of individuals who experience homelessness and unemployment not only because of mental illness, but also as a consequence of income and other personal problems.

---

[1] These are type A cooperatives working for the public services with professional educators. Type B cooperatives are those that have at least 30% of clients as their members.

# KEY ELEMENTS OF THE WORKING STYLE

## People with Severe Mental Illness have the Civil Right to Live in a Normal House

The take-home lesson of the psychiatric hospitals closure is that even people considered as chronically addicted to institutions can live in normal houses and adapt to community life, without the need of more restrictive residential programs. The opportunity for a mental patient to exercise the right to live in a place of his choice, for example an apartment, with the necessary home support, is the premise for clinical and life quality improvement. The switch from theory to practice is warranted by the attribution of a real house to the patient with the necessary effective home support from the staff. In other words, the procedure involves giving power back to patients by means of real life choices and decision-making possibilities. A house (or better, a home) chosen by the patient is considered in our experience to be a prerequisite for any kind of therapeutic and rehabilitative approach. It is the place where the patient receives support and help from the staff and where s/he gains the possibility of exercising the right to live in a house regardless of psychiatric diagnosis. The possibility to live in a stable house changes her/his perspective: s/he becomes the occupier of a real apartment just like any other normal citizen. The citizen role is essential for promoting inclusion into community life and offers the patients the possibility of being asked to perform normal tasks requested by a normal environment.

In our experience, even severe mental patients are able to cope with life in the community if adequately supported.

## New Way of Interaction Between Patients and Staff by Paying Attention to Patients' Point of View

The interaction between all staff members (psychiatrists, psychologists, nurses, social workers, educators and non-professionals) and patients must rely upon a new basis which is different from the clinical approach based on a mere analysis of clinical symptoms and diagnosis. These two elements are both potentially very influential in terms of clinical outcome.

The alternative approach relies upon the consideration of patients as human beings, an apparently simple concept however revolutionary in the field, and for this reason it is difficult to be accepted. A simple approach is to identify and empower those aspects of the patient's life/personality not involved in the disease and by this to enable them to live in the community.

The starting point in the rehabilitation process implemented in the former psychiatric hospital was the switch from "patient" to "person". This apparently simple operation was performed by the psychiatric teams by collecting and reconstructing the stories of each individual and by paying careful attention to the needs and wishes of every patient. Initially, the plans of the day were conducted through team meetings, where the plans were elaborated and discussed and the results verified, sometimes after exhausting discussions. The meetings were also the arena in which the operators had the chance to present their points of view gathered from long experience in the field and close contacts with the patients. On the other side, experience was shared with the whole group and directly used for implementing a new working style and for assuming complete responsibility of the patients' therapeutic plan.

This choice of new interaction was the leading approach for people who had been hospitalized for more than 50 years and were not ready to face the challenge of living in a house outside the Hospital. Consideration of the personality of the patients was the basis for establishing positive interactions with the staff. This attributed a new role to patients, who become active parts of the project and not merely a target of medical treatments. Discussion with the individual patients on their specific treatment program was aimed at gaining participation and cooperation, which is highly beneficial for clinical outcome. This issue was stressed also with the more difficult patients who were reluctant to undertake the necessary efforts to participate by individual negotiation. In our daily work in the Rehabilitation Program, patients' engagement was considered as a predictor of clinical outcome. For this reason, realistic or alternative options should be provided also in the "difficult" cases, to convince the patients of the benefits of mutually shared efforts.

There is a common assumption that mental patients do not have the ability to make correct decisions, even if such decisions concern very personal choices and situations. This issue may become detrimental in the process of re-acquisition of personal individuality and generate dependency relationships (Chamberlain, 1997). It is necessary to provide a wide range of options (e.g. where do you prefer living? do you want to live alone?) which represent the real watershed in changing the life quality of patients.

One of the major changes needed for fulfilling the needs of severe mental patients concerns the role played by psychiatrists. Severe mental patients have needs that range from mere medical treatment to the need for a complex and multi-faceted project involving several aspects of daily life. In fact it is still quite difficult to involve psychiatrists in those aspects not directly linked to medical and pharmacological treatments.

## Staff Organization for Home Support

Another key issue is the ratio between staff and number of patients to manage. Staff groups are ideally small (10 operators for 50-60 patients in independent living), although the common experience, also shared by us, indicates that a slight under-staffing may generate motivation, participation and a sense of responsibility to the entire group (Nelson et al., 1988).

The staff must be oriented to function as a learning organization, self-asking key questions (what is it? and what it ought to be?) and including continuous internal controls on the results obtained after evaluation of the action plans. All forms of evaluation must take place in an organizational concept, originating from the mandatory need of a continuously changing organization (Richards, 1992).

Shifting service delivery to patients' homes, as previously done in the rehabilitation program, implies mandatory changes in the organization of the Community Mental Health Centres.

People with mental illness have special needs, which also change in time and in quality. As a consequence, the service organization must adapt its performances to patients' needs and not vice versa. The motto is to serve people *where* they live and *when* they need.

These issues should receive adequate responses from psychiatric services, namely the Community Mental Health Centres, by adopting a strategy characterized by few but essential rules:

i) Centres must provide flexible and individualized assistance to be delivered, when necessary, at the patient's home.
ii) Centres must take into consideration the changing needs of the patients. This does not mean passive adaptation to non-constructive requests, but flexible responses to needs of patients living outside residential programs. The effect is a marked reduction of transfer of patients to custodial situations.
iii) Centres must be ready to maintain support indefinitely, in order to maximize opportunities for patients' success in independent living.
iv) Centres should provide assistance on a 24-hour basis, activating all possible community resources.

These results may be achieved through rapid and efficient planning undertaken by the staff themselves. The staff organization needs daily meetings, where operators can exchange all necessary information about the patients under their care. Careful attention must be paid to operators' visit reports. Another qualifying element of the group is a shared understanding of values and principles underpinning "good care for the patient with severe and enduring mental distress.

## Access to Information and Tenures

Another, and not less significant, mission of the Community Mental Health Centres is to inform patients about their rights and make them practically accessible. A house is a general and commonly shared desire and living in a house is also preferred by service users (Tanzman, 1993; Goering et al., 1990).

It is still not clear which agency or authority should take responsibility for the housing projects and for supporting patients living independently. Ideally, all agencies involved in planning and providing different services should work together and plan strategically. Italy is burdened with a bureaucratic apparatus which hampers any constructive activity and utilises an incredible amount of economic resources. Front-line operators face difficulties and frustration when working with the different agencies. Lack of synergy and coordinated actions among different institutional partners (e.g. social services, public housing agencies, and mental care) are a consequence of a lack of specific culture to deal with real problems which are even more problematic when the roles and priorities of these different services are still unclear.

Mental patients generally lack the necessary information to obtain financial support from the social services or from the Mental Health Department. The insidious bureaucratic machinery lacks the ability to provide rapid responses and its intrinsic complexity, incomprehensible to ordinary people, *de facto* excludes many patients from access to these rights. A significant portion of the coordination among the different agencies is relying more on talented or committed individuals rather than the organisation of the system. This is undoubtedly an unprofessional approach; but at this moment it is apparently the only one overcoming the limits of the system.

Currently there is general consensus that staff should find resources and synergies with private and public institutions as well as charities in order to integrate the decreasing funds allocated by the National Health System.

### Help and Advice in the Management of Personal Money and Belongings

This has been another essential issue in our daily work in the rehabilitation experience but which is still quite difficult to achieve in standard community care. This support needs to be formalized in a "contract" between the patient and the staff. It is aimed at providing the patients with the necessary financial independence which allows them to live in a house without the need of external family or state support. Help in managing personal money may also have a preventive effect on patients' crisis.

The acceptance of this kind of help comes some times after long discussions and is continuously adapted and renewed in the light of the patient's situation.

### Promotion of Service Users' Association Activities

Last but not less important in the process of patients becoming full-rights citizens is the relation with the service users association, an approach that the Community Mental Health Centres are now activating, albeit very slowly.

Critical in the psychiatric hospital closure program was the shift from a virtual entitlement of basic civil rights to the possibility of transferring them into practice: the feeling and confidence to trigger a chain of events that originates in having the right to do something in order to realize a personal desire (Corbascio, 2002). This was the challenging and innovative task of service users associations. Non-professional operators working to support service users associations transferred daily stimulating hints to the patients in order to revive and develop their ability to control and to deal with everyday endeavours. The Association was acting as a real trade union for users and at the same time as a tool for the exercise of their rights.

The advocacy role of service users' associations in contemporary mental health services has become an increasingly important factor in developing more responsive services and in the creation of a broad network promoting social inclusion. A constructive competition between different operators and users yields the intrinsic result of improving the quality provided by the different services involved with patient care.

## Concluding Remarks

The reasons why the over-viewed guidelines and working style are still not fully accomplished by the Community Mental Health Centres of our Department are multiple.

The most important is cultural i.e. the lack of previous experience in anti-institutional work for the majority of the junior nurses, operators and psychiatrists; a second issue is of a structural nature: the increasing number of patients needing to be treated in such a complex way is often not organizationally sustained.

The rehabilitation approach should be considered as new land in psychiatry, considering its intrinsic potential to modify radically the actual practices of mental health services.

Is this academic speculation or might it become reality? The general issue could be answered by considering rehabilitation not as a specialized technique for those patients with special needs, e.g. the so-called chronic patients usually with a past history of long hospitalizations. Secondly, rehabilitation must not be separated from Community Care services or confined to a special sector of psychiatric care, as is the case for several Mental Health Departments of this country. Thirdly, rehabilitation should be adopted for all those patients who have suffered the direct and indirect consequences of psychiatric disease. Mental patients are to be considered *de facto* individuals in a peculiar condition that limits the possibilities and rights of their existence.

In conclusion, rehabilitation moves beyond the basic principles of psychotherapeutic approaches which essentially treat mental disease through words and symbols. The rehabilitation models require that M.D.s and operators do things WITH patients rather than merely talking to/with them. The aim of rehabilitation is to leave the service building and offices and operate where the lives of our patients face daily challenges, i.e. at home, in the workplace and on the street. The elimination of the no-man's land, where the differences between normal lives and those of psychiatric patients become apparent, is expected to lower the needs for segregation under any name that one calls it. The important clinical successes achieved by rehabilitation techniques clearly indicate the necessity for overcoming the ideological and philosophical separation between treatment and rehabilitation.

## REFERENCES

Basaglia, F. (1968): *L'Istituzione Negata*; Torino: Einaudi.

Carrucciu, M.A./Corbascio, G. C./Ghiori, L./Henry, P./Lenoci, F./Naldi R. (1995): Che cosa Abbiamo Imparato nel Superamento dell'Ospedale Psichiatrico di Grugliasco; in: *Fogli di Informazi*one, 166, 15-19.

CENSIS (1994): Le Poltiche Psichiatriche Regionali nel Dopo Riforma e lo Stato Attuale dei Servizi; Roma: Censis.

Chamberlain, J. A. (1997): Working Definition of Empowerment; in: *Psychiatric Rehabilitation Journal*, Vol. 20, n. 4, 43-46, Boston.

Corbascio, G. C./Henry, P. (1994): How can Psychiatric Hospitals Survive? The Italian Experience; in: *International Journal of Social Psychiatry* 40, 269-276.

Corbascio, G. C. (2002): Closing a Psychiatric Hospital for Opening a New Perspective of the Mental Illness – an Italian Experience; in Ramon, S. (ed.) *European Perspectives of Mental Health Promotion: First Steps,* Cambridge: Anglia University Press.

Corbascio, G. C. (2003): Case vere o Strutture?; in: *Fogli di Informazione*, 197, 118-123.

Goering, R./Paduchak, D./Durbin J. (1990): Housing Homeless Women: A Consumer Preference Study; in: *Hospital and Community Psychiatry* 41, 6, 790-794.

Mezzina, R. (2003): La globalizzazione e la Sfida per I Servizi di Salute Mentale; in: *Fogli di Informazione*, 197, 156-173.

Nelson, G./Walsh, L./Bowers, G./Hall, B. (1988): Housing for Psychiatric Survivors: Values, Policy and Research; in: *Admin Policy Mental Health*, 25, 4, 455-462.

Pirella, A. (1987): The Implementation of the Italian Psychiatric Reform in a Large Conurbation; in: *International Journal of Social Psychiatry*, 33, 2, 119-131.

Pirella, A. (1999): *Il Problema Psichiatrico*; Italy: Centro di Documentazione di Pistoia.

Richards, H. (1992): *Quality Assurance through Observation of Service Delivery*; London: Kings Fund College.

Scarpa S. (1974): *La Pratica della Follia*; Gorizia, Italy, June 22: First Congress of Psichiatria Democratica.

Tanzam, B. (1993): An Overview of Surveys of Mental Health Consumers: Preferences for Housing and Support Services; in: *Hospital and Community Psychiatry*, 44 (5) 450-455.

World Health Organisation Report (2001): – *World Health Report – Mental Health: New Understanding, New Hope*; WHO, Geneva, Switzerland, 2001.

In: Knowledge in Mental Health
Editors: L.Sapouna and P. Herrmann, pp. 85-99
ISBN 1-59454-812-9


*Chapter 6*

# Tracing Evidence of Institutionalisation in the Process of De-Institutionalisation – The Irish Case

***Lydia Sapouna***
Department of Applied Social Studies University College Cork, Ireland

## Abstract

In discussing the nature of evaluation in mental health care and examining the construction of 'valid evidence', this chapter will focus on a type of evidence which is consistently ignored in Irish mental health policy. This concerns the continuation of institutional patterns of thinking and practising and the severe violation of human rights experienced by people suffering from mental distress. The discrepancies between the scandalous conditions of care and the unreserved heralding of progressive changes will be examined. Furthermore I will trace components/indicators of institutionalisation in mental health policy and practice. While the discussion is based on the Irish system, its aim is not to construct Irish mental health as a pathological model of care but rather to highlight how institutionalisation can be reproduced through 'reform' policies that fail to take a broader view of mental distress. This question is of universal rather than local relevance. To conclude, the concept of institutionalisation will be re-defined in terms of policy, practice and broader political considerations.

## Setting the Scene

I did my social work training in Greece in a period when the 'scandal' of Leros psychiatric hospital was at its peak. The exposure of the inhuman and shocking conditions of custodial psychiatry brought about a big controversy amongst professional groups and the broader public, and provided the driving force for a reform in the mental health sector. A five-year mental health plan was devised within the context of European Community funding towards the development of psychiatric rehabilitation services (EC, Regulation 815, 1984). Since 1984 there has been a significant reform movement which was also quite politicised.[1] The 80s was a time of change in Greek mental health, and while the institutional tradition and the centrality of the medical model were by no means displaced, a number of innovative ideas and projects were developed.

After gaining experience in mental health social work in Greece, I went to Ireland in the early 1990s to do research in the area of de-institutionalisation and community care for adults with mental health problems. My initial expectations were that I would learn from good practice, believing that I would certainly have the opportunity to study different, if not more 'advanced' developments. Such expectations were probably the product of a typical southern European inferiority syndrome, where 'western' forms of social organisation and practice are regularly assumed to be far superior and more advanced. However, I was faced with a rather different reality. The process of de-institutionalisation was being implemented but to a large extent community care evolved, both physically and ideologically, in the grounds of big Victorian institutions. Mental health in Ireland is perhaps one of the most marginal and under-resourced areas in social service provision and in the practice of social professions. Hospital admissions are still regulated by the 1945 Mental Treatment Act, a legislation that does not fulfil Ireland's commitments under a number of international agreements. Community care services, such as day care services and community residences, are both underdeveloped and under-utilised, with their primary emphasis being on ensuring safety through compliance with treatment rather than interaction with the community. This situation is both maintained and exacerbated by the absence of a public debate on issues concerning mental health problems and their treatment in Irish society.

Encountering these conditions made me question the point of my exercise. What can be learned from the absence of good practice? It took me time to realise that studying the Irish attachment to institutional forms of practice could provide valuable insights. One particularly challenging task was finding the tools to evaluate de-institutionalisation projects such as re-socialisation and day care units. As my hypothesis was that institutional practice is reproduced in the process of de-institutionalisation, I had to consider the nature of evidence that would support such a claim. A significant part of the study was an inquiry into the 'making' and application of knowledge in the areas of de-institutionalisation and community mental health. Through this inquiry it was possible to consider the micro-level of practising de-institutionalisation by focusing on themes such as the quality of interaction between service users and professionals, an indicator largely ignored in the dominant technicist evaluation frameworks. It was also possible to consider the macro-level of policy-making and critically explore the nature of the measures that have been heralded as 'improvements' in mental health care (see Sapouna, 1993; Leane and Sapouna, 1998). This latter consideration will be the primary focus of this chapter.

A central theme in this book is the nature of evidence in mental health service evaluation. In Irish mental health, the evidence of human rights abuse is overwhelming. "Nowhere in Irish society are human rights more systematically abused than in mental institutions and nowhere are these abuses more ignored" (Brown, 2001: 20). While there has been no systematic evaluation of community care, every year the Report of the Inspector of Mental

---

[1] For a comprehensive account of the mental health reform program in Greece see Madianos and Yfantopoulos (1984), Stefanis, Madianos & Giltelman (1986), Strutti and Rauber (1994), Yfantopoulos (1994).

Hospitals is published. Every year it reveals shocking conditions in mental hospitals throughout the country and abuses of the rights of patients in these hospitals. Every year this report is systematically ignored at both political and policy levels.

The state of mental health services is now explicitly identified as a cause of concern by an internationally recognised body for human rights. In February 2003 the Irish Branch of Amnesty International launched a campaign on mental illness with the publication of the report *Mental Illness: the Neglected Quarter*. The report argues that the Irish Government has failed to act on a series of national and international reports critical of its inaction in respecting the human rights of people with mental illness. Amnesty's report reveals that services in Ireland are slow, inadequate, inconsistent in their application throughout the country, and severely under-resourced in terms of staff, money and available therapies. Mental health services for children and adolescents, the homeless, prisoners, and other vulnerable groups are particularly deficient. To date there has been no indication that the content of this report has been taken into consideration. A prime example of the state's indifference towards the conditions of mental health care is the government's reaction to the Annual Report of the Inspector of Mental Hospitals for the year 1998 (Department of Health and Children, 1999). This report suggested that the state has been involved in the wilful and possibly criminal neglect of vulnerable people in its care and that, because of such neglect, citizens have died. It further revealed that citizens continue to be deprived of their liberty, often without elementary inquiry into the justification of such deprivation. The 'response' of the Department of Health to this shocking report was: "*The health services aim to achieve the best quality of life for each individual through the provision of high-quality, patient-centred services, and the work of the Inspectorate helps to ensure that high standards are maintained in our mental health services*" (Cowen, 1999).

This chapter examines the discrepancy between the indisputable violation of human rights in Irish mental health care and the heralding of progressive changes such as new legislation, primary care and advocacy. The discussion highlights the marginal place mental health occupies within the health and social care system and the continuation of institutional forms of thinking and practising in both hospital and community settings. However, while the focus is on the Irish system, this situation is not just an Irish problem. The question of 'institutionalisation' is one of universal relevance and the Irish example is perhaps an excellent opportunity to consider it and re-define it by acknowledging its complex and subtle manifestations.

## The Policy and Political Context

### Mental Health Policy

In Ireland, as elsewhere, the concepts of de-institutionalisation and community care underpin the policy and practice of mental health care. Significant progress has occurred since the publication of the *Report of the Commission of Enquiry in Mental Illness* in 1966, which criticised the predominant institutional response to mental illness and recommended the development of community care structures. Indeed, during the past three decades the number of the inpatient population has declined and a range of community-based facilities have developed.[2] However, it will be shown that mental health services are still dominated by institutional patterns of thinking and practising.

The Expert Group on Mental Health Policy was established in 2003, to prepare a new national policy framework for the mental health services, updating the 1984 policy document Planning for the Future. The group consists of eighteen people with a wide and diverse range of experience in the area of mental health. The process of developing the new framework indicates a willingness to recognise the expertise of previously unheard and traditionally discredited voices of service users, relatives and carers. This is evident in the representation of the Irish Advocacy Network in the Group and the broad consultation process with all concerned with the development of mental health policy. The findings from the consultation process provide a very clear indication of service users' views in relation to the present state of the mental health services and how they should be developed in the future (see www.mentalhealth policy.ie).

At the time of writing this chapter the report of the Expert Group has not been yet published. It is expected to be launched in early 2006 proposing a mental health service which is service user centred, recovery oriented, holistic and community based. While these proposals indicate a promising and much needed shift in service provision we need to remember that a community based approach is by no means a 'new' policy in Ireland.

The framework for community mental health is outlined in *Planning for the Future,* a policy document published in 1984 following a major review of psychiatric services carried out between 1981 and 1984. In summary, the report set out guidelines for future development as far as possible in a community setting, with the emphasis on resources being transferred from large psychiatric hospitals to a large range of alternative community-based services and to acute units in general hospitals. Among the key elements in the planning framework were:

- the location of services close to where people work, and a strong emphasis on outpatient care.
- the provision of inpatient treatment in psychiatric units in general hospitals, with the role of the traditional psychiatric hospital diminishing as alternative community-based services are developed.
- the provision of high-support hostels for a small number who will require long-term inpatient care, and the provision of appropriate housing in the community.
- services to be provided on a sectoral basis for a given population by a multidisciplinary team to be based in each sector.

Ironically, while many aspects of this policy are considered outdated, a number of its targets remain under-implemented. A critical review of *Planning for the Future* and its implementation is provided later in this chapter. The 1994 health strategy *Shaping a Healthier Future* recommended that "mental health services should be comprehensive, integrated with other health services, based as far as possible in the community and organised in sectors close to the people being served". In 1998, the Department of Health and Children published the *Guidelines for Good Practice and Quality Assurance in Mental Health Services.* Their emphasis on the patient as consumer and the duty to provide "the highest level of mental

[2] A full picture of these developments is provided by the Annual Health Statistics Reports, published by the Department of Health and Children and the Annual Reports of the Inspector of Mental Hospitals.

health care possible" also remain under-observed (Amnesty International, 2003). The 2001 national health strategy *Quality and Fairness/A Health System for You* took a primary care approach, advocating the development of integrated health care and making a commitment to increasing community care facilities. This approach aims to facilitate the development of primary care responses to mental illness and the treatment of mental illness in general health care. More specifically, the 2001 Health Strategy proposed the introduction of an inter-disciplinary team-based approach to primary care provision. Members of the primary care team will include GPs, nurses/midwives, health care assistants, home helps, physiotherapists, occupational therapists, social workers and administrative personnel. A wider network of other care professionals such as speech and language therapists, community pharmacists, dieticians, community welfare officers, dentists, chiropodists and psychologists will also provide services for the enrolled population of each primary care team. At the time of writing this chapter, the implementation of the new health strategy recommendations for primary care and the reform of health services remain under-observed.

The lack of a concrete resource commitment has been the main explanation for the inaction upon the above policies between professional and policy circles. Amnesty International's report *Mental Illness: the Neglected Quarter* (2003) highlighted that the mental health sector has been preferentially hit by cutbacks in the 1980s. In a re-appraisal of the closing of mental hospital beds in 1993, Dr. Marcus Webb stated that "the share of gross expenditure provided in Ireland for the psychiatric services has been reduced by 20% since 1976. This slide must be halted and reversed if this country is to preserve a semblance of mature and civilised care for its mentally ill" (Webb 1993, in Amnesty International, 2003:54). However, since then the situation has not been reversed and revenue expenditure in mental health has remained disproportionately low. "While overall growth in Irish non-capital health expenditure between 1990 and 2001 was over 300 per cent, that of the psychiatric programme was 131 per cent, by far the lowest. In 1994, mental health spending accounted for 9.4 per cent of total health non-capital expenditure; by 2001, it was just 7.2 per cent" (Amnesty International, 2003:54).

Poor resource allocation is a broader issue, however. It is an indication of poor political will to deal with people with mental distress in a way other than exclusion. This is evident in the failure of the 'reform policies' to take a broader view of mental distress and to change the power imbalances between service users and professionals through a more participatory form of service development and delivery. A brief examination of health politics can provide some useful insights.

## Health Politics: 'Value for Money', Consumerism and Mental Health Reform

The aim of this discussion is not to highlight the need to act upon an overall inclusive and fair mental health policy but rather to raise some concerns regarding the nature of the proposed changes and the broader political context of health care. One such concern was noted by the UN Committee on Economic Social and Cultural Rights (CESCR) who noted "with regret that a human rights framework encompassing, *inter alia*, the principles of non-discrimination and equal access to health facilities and services was not embodied in the ...National Health Strategy" (CESCR, 2002 in Amnesty International, 2003:53).

This is a manifestation of a political climate within which the provision of health services is guided by a 'value for money' principle and a managerial approach to service structure,[3] rather than a commitment to an equitable health system. As one health board official put it "*as a Chief Executive Officer of a Health Board I am a manager of a business. It is as simple as that. If health is a business, then value for money is what is going to drive that business from now on*" (Sean Hurley, in the "Irish Examiner" 28 April 2003). Part of this trend involves what Offe (1984) referred to as the 'commodification' of welfare services, a process incorporating market principles into the health service. In a context where economic effectiveness and efficiency become state priorities "there has been a widespread acceptance of privatising the impacts of poverty, lack of education, isolation and neglect of those who are unable to contribute economically" (Rioux, 2002: 218). Rioux further argues that this trend had a significant impact on people with disabilities, leading to disability being privatised. A similar argument can be made for mental health. In Ireland, a shrinking public health service fails to provide much beyond hospital-based acute psychiatric care where human and citizenship rights are consistently violated. While the new health strategy (2001) emphasises the need to move beyond medical perspectives of mental health, Ireland remains the only country in Europe without a position of a consultant psychotherapist working in the psychiatric system. 'Alternative' therapies, including psychotherapy and counselling, can be accessed only privately and are not refundable by either public or private health insurance schemes, a situation rendering mental health a private rather than a public good.

In this political context 'value for money' and deficit reduction is argued to be a greater social good than social justice and basic rights (see Kuttner, 1984). While the development of the Irish health system has not been influenced by a commitment to universal provision and social justice (see Barrington, 1987; Curry, 2003; Powell, 1992; Fanning, 1999), a health reform has the potential to address such limitations. However, this does not seem to be the case as the narrow perspectives of efficiency and profitability replace these potential goals. As Arora (2001) argues, "health is not simply turned into a business with growing access on market orientation; implicit in this process is its loss of status as a right. It is this denial of meaning of citizenship through a denial of even basic rights that is the most disturbing implication of project liberalisation" (Arora, 2001:31-32).

A discussion on the inequalities of the Irish health system[4] and the implications of the marketisation of health services goes beyond the purpose of this chapter. However, it is important to understand the impact of these trends in shaping the context where mental health policy and practice take place. Through this understanding it will be possible to consider whether institutional patterns of exclusion have changed through the proposed policy reforms by: (a) taking a broader view of mental distress and (b) increasing service user participation in mental health policy and practice.

---

3 Such trends can be clearly identified in the Value for Money Audit carried by Deloitte & Touche on behalf of the Department of Health and Children (2001), and the 2001 Health Strategy.

4 A comprehensive discussion on the questions of accessibility and equity in Irish health care is provided by Maev-Ann Wren in her book 'Unhealthy State' (2003).

# A Broader View of Mental Health?

## Community Care Policy and Practice

This chapter has already provided evidence of the continuous under-funding of mental health services in Ireland. I also argue that as long as 'value for money' priorities dominate health care, there is limited scope for changes that move beyond improvements in buildings and management structures. If 'value for money' is the guiding principle in the provision of health care, how are community-based/holistic forms of mental health practice 'priced'? Community care is not necessarily the 'cheap alternative' to institutions. Implementing de-institutionalisation requires a concrete resource commitment which has not been evident in the Irish case. However, the type of commitment required for community care to work goes beyond the question of monetary value. It also relates to appreciating the value of community care as an ideology and practice. Unfortunately, as the *Report of the Inspector of Mental Hospitals* for 2002 reveals, the value of community care is still not recognised by many professionals. "There still continues to be on the part of many psychiatrists and others difficulty in comprehending and effecting the benefits of community care in all its ramifications. This understanding or the lack of it leads to an over-reliance on in-patient care and a reluctance to move out into the community" (Department of Health and Children, 2003:7).

In reviewing the transition towards community-based mental health, I have already argued that many of the targets set by *Planning for the Future* (1984) remain under-implemented and that many of its recommendations are considered outdated. A further point I wish to make concerns the way in which 'mental illness' is viewed in this document. While *Planning for the Future* advocates for community mental health, it fails to challenge the dominant medical model and the way mental illness is constructed and treated within this model. As a result it fails to consider the broader factors that affect the incidence and diagnosis of 'mental illness'. As Butler (1987) argued "*Planning for the Future* is above all a medical report; that is, it is based on the implicit assumption that the planning of the psychiatric services is merely a matter of assessing the prevalence of mental illness and establishing the structures which best facilitate the delivery of modern scientific treatment methods" (1987:48). This policy is primarily a debate of relocation and modernisation of the existing services through administrative restructuring rather than a debate that considers broader policy issues. An examination of the trends in psychiatric provision during the past 20 years may provide some further insights into the practice of community mental health. The following table maps the developments in this area.

**Trends in Psychiatric Provision, 1984-2001**

| | All Psychiatric Hospitals and Units | | Day Facilities | | Hostels | |
|---|---|---|---|---|---|---|
| | Admissions | Patients | No. | Places | No. | Places |
| 1984 | 28,330 | 11,613 | 32 | 800 | 121 | 900 |
| 1993 | 27,005 | 6,657 | 145 | 2,556 | 361 | 2,556 |
| 1998 | 25,158 | 4,340 | 175 | 3,361 | 380 | 2,850 |
| 2001 | 24,446 | 4,321 | 179 | 3,653 | 404 | 3,077 |

**Source:** Health Research Board.

As this table shows, the number of patients admitted to psychiatric hospitals declined significantly between the years 1984 and 2001. A considerable development in community facilities such as day centres and residential care has also taken place. However, while the number of patients was reduced by more than fifty per cent for the period 1984-2001, the same argument can not be made for the number of admissions. A consistent high rate of admissions indicates a high re-admission rate, amounting for 70% of all admissions in 2001 (Daly & Walsh, 2002). This is a reflection of two closely linked factors: the over-reliance on inpatient care and the lack of adequate community care facilities.

Community mental health is still not the norm in Ireland. For example, in 1998 only one third of first admissions took place in psychiatric wards located in general hospitals, and in 2001 less than half of the first admissions took place in such a setting. Furthermore, it has to be stressed that the physical integration of psychiatry with general medicine does not necessarily guarantee an open, or indeed a less institutional, care environment. A prime example of how such relocation may perpetuate or even intensify segregation is a newly established psychiatric ward in Cork city which has been heralded as 'a model of de-institutionalisation' following the closure of an isolated psychiatric unit in a suburb of the city. While this unit is part of a centrally located general hospital, it is in the meantime a separate highly secured section of the overall building. The Inspector of Mental Hospitals highlighted, after the 2000 Inspection, that "the entrance to the unit was locked and security was provided on a twenty-four hour basis. Also, its location on the first floor without any outdoor space for the patients constituted a major difficulty" (2001: 163). Four years after, the Inspectorate's recommendations for less intimidating security presence and access to open space and fresh air for the patients of this unit have not yet been implemented.

There is also a considerable variation between regions in the availability of community mental health services, with some catchment areas having no multidisciplinary teams. The over-reliance on acute hospital units was also highlighted by a Health Research Board (HRB) study *We have no Beds* on the availability and use of acute psychiatric beds in the Eastern Health Board (Keogh, Roche & Walsh, 1999). The findings of the study showed that there is an adequate number of acute psychiatric beds, but an inadequate number of these beds were available for acute psychiatric use, with 45% of these acute beds occupied by non-acute patients. The same study also found that there was a shortage of day hospital places and that many day hospitals were not operating as alternatives or complements to acute inpatient care. The lack of fully and equally distributed community-based facilities has been a concern of the Mental Health Inspectorate for a number of years. The absence of such facilities reduces the sources of support for people in mental distress to inpatient care. An interesting observation, made by both the Inspector of Mental Hospitals' report for 1998 and the 1999 HRB study, concerned the excessive use of inpatient units for assessment of patients. "Community-based mental health centres were inadequate and unequally distributed throughout the catchment area and even where they were in place, assessment of patients, particularly in relation to possible inpatient care or its alternatives, was rarely carried out there. As a result many patients presented to the inpatient unit for assessment, thus making inappropriate admissions more likely" (HRB, 1999: 109). A more recent HRB research highlighted that day care options are not utilised to their full potential. The findings of this study, published in 2003 in a publication entitled *"Psychiatric Day Care-An Underused Option?"*, showed that many psychiatric day hospitals and day centres were occupying premises unsuitable for day care purposes and did not provide a comprehensive range of treatments. Additionally, returning to a point made earlier, "many mental health professionals...had limited perceptions of the role of a day hospital and what type of illness could be treated at such a facility" (Hickey, Moran and Walsh, 2003:7).

This is some further evidence of the continuous commitment to institutional forms of thinking and practising as mental health policy and professional practice have failed to take a broader view of mental distress. This is also evident in the new mental health legislation.

## The Legal Status of Community Care

*Planning for the Future* is a policy document, not a legal framework. That means that it states the desirable way to deal with mental health problems but it does not allow the explicit right to be treated in the community. In other words, there is not a statutory obligation to provide mental health services in line with current policies.

Admissions to psychiatric hospitals are still regulated by the 1945 Mental Treatment Act. The Mental Health Act was passed in 2001 and has not yet been fully implemented. The 1945 Mental Treatment Act was considered a major innovative piece of legislation in its time, as it signalled a shift away from the previous 'legal' attitude to mental health care towards a medically based model (see Guckian, 1998). For example, the Act allowed for the first time the admission of 'voluntary' patients to psychiatric hospitals. A legal reform was necessary as the current criteria for detention in Ireland do not conform to those required by the country's international commitments, particularly the European Convention for the Protection of Human Rights and Fundamental Freedoms (1950), the UN Principles for the Protection of Persons with Mental Illness and the Improvement of Mental Health Care (1991) and the Recommendations of the Council of Europe.

The 2001 Mental Health Act attempts to restore some of the long neglected rights of people with mental health problems in Ireland. However, it fails to provide for the inclusion of people with mental health problems in Irish society. The primary concern of the Act is detention; and in particular involuntary admissions, and the rights of involuntary patients. The debate is clearly located within inpatient care of a compulsory nature and fails to provide a broader representation of the mental health sufferer, making no reference to the rights of voluntary clients and the rights of people receiving treatment in the community. It is ironic that while the Act re-constructs the position of the 'Inspector of Mental Hospitals', to 'Inspector of Mental Health Services', these services are very narrowly defined as those under the clinical direction of a consultant psychiatrist. This represents a narrow, medical view of mental health services, which as Keys (2002) argues "may prevent the Inspector from having the authority to visit independent services not under the control of a consultant psychiatrist. This issue has been raised by some interested organisations...to try to ensure that there was some supervisory control in the provision of accommodation or work-related services by independent providers" (Keys, 2002:70).

The forthcoming legislation has been heralded as a discourse of 'change' in mental health care. However, it does not reflect a commitment to ensuring 'patient' rights in the community and it does not deal with the picture of mental illness with any broad vision. It is more like a necessary administrative/regulatory provision which may bring this state in line with the kind of protective provisions that have long been available in other European countries. Therefore, this discourse does not seem to be a meaningful step for the relocation of people with mental health problems in the community. On the contrary, sufferers' rights are secured outside the community, as the status of the involuntary patient seems to be a precondition to qualify for such rights. Within such an approach, service users remain in the place of the 'other' and can only be passive recipients of care and control rather than active citizens with the right to be involved in service development and provision.

## The Mental Health Service User: Consumer or Participant?

The importation of market principles into health care has created a space for a consideration of the mental health service user as a person with entitlements within this market place. Pilgrim and Rogers (1999) describe this as an alternative way of conceptualising psychiatric patients as 'consumers' of services rather than objects of clinical intervention. "The term 'consumerism' implies the existence of choice between products, and an active insistence on value for money" (Pilgrim and Rogers, 1999:165). This consumer definition does not question the biomedical basis of psychiatry, nor does it encompass a more democratic ethos in service provision. It does, however, provide the space to consider the patient as a person with entitlements, and this transformation contains the potential for resistance (see Speed, 2002a). The question is whether the shift to community care in Ireland has led to the development of sites where institutional forms of thinking and practising can be resisted. In order to address this question, I will briefly consider (i) the role of service user research in constructing a platform for their experiences to be heard and validated and (ii) the nature of service user involvement in their care plan.

## Service User-led Research

In a discussion on Irish mental health social movements, Speed (2002b) argues that contrary to the UK, Irish mental health organisations have been much more closely tied into the mental health service system. The dominant type of organisations have been *for* users of services such as AWARE and Schizophrenia Ireland. However, during the last three years there has been a significant move for some representation *of* users *by* users.[5] One vehicle through which the views of service users can be heard is their involvement in mental health research projects. The contribution of service user research in the construction of evidence in mental health care evaluation is discussed by Shulamit Ramon in her chapter on pages 101 ff. While I do not intend to cover this topic comprehensively, I wish to highlight some issues related to the nature of service user participation in Irish mental health research. In the limited literature available, I can identify in particular the concerns raised by Speed (2002b) through his involvement in two user-led mental health research projects in Ireland as a research co-ordinator. Speed, drawing on Beresford's and Wallcraft's model of emancipatory research (1997), argues that in his experience, Irish user-led mental health research "is composed of

[5] For example the Irish Advocacy Network is a user run user led organisation providing information and support to fellow mental health service users, to empower them to speak up and take control of their own lives. Cork Advocacy Network is an also organisation working for better mental health care in the Cork region. It was initially set up by a group of families with a son or daughter caught up in the revolving door of the psychiatric system.

mental health service users acting as paid and unpaid consultants and researchers for non-statutory and statutory mental health organisations" (Speed, 2002b:2). This form of involvement is obviously a significant step, as it may signify a shift of power from mental health professionals and organisations to service users themselves. For example, for the purpose of reviewing its mental health services one health board commissioned the Irish Advocacy Network to undertake work, offering users of mental health services an opportunity to input into the review. In total 163 semi-structured in-depth interviews were held with users of mental health services in two counties. The outcome of the review was a report published in 2002. This exercise is certainly an innovative step in the Irish mental health context; nevertheless it should not be confused with research controlled *by* service users. In this model we have an organisation *for* service users, doing research *of* service users, conducted *by* service users (see Speed, 2002b). I found reading the report a somewhat disappointing experience, as the views of service users are hardly prominent in the discussion of the findings. In other words, there was very limited information on what was actually heard during the consultation process. Speed raises some concerns in relation to this type of participation in service user research, as empowerment can be reduced to simply "letting the service users construct a questionnaire, administer and analyse data" (2002a: 3), rather than effecting social change within the lives/situations of service users. As these projects have been recently completed their impact remains to be seen. However, despite the concerns raised in the previous discussion the contribution of such research is not to be undermined, as it can be a tool to empower service users[6] and challenge the monopoly of the medical profession in the management of their condition. The importance of service user involvement and peer-advocacy is now recognised by governmental policy. The 2001 health strategy recommends that "independent patient advocacy services will be encouraged and resourced" (Department of Health and Children, 2001a:72). Indeed, since September 2002 the Department of Health has been funding the posts of regional advocates in five health board areas, which is certainly a positive step.

Nevertheless, while this is a significant shift towards a more 'inclusive' form of mental health care, there is enough evidence to suggest that service users still experience exclusion at different levels of service provision. The following discussion will consider how this exclusion manifests itself in the areas of information and consultation and the involvement of service users in their care plan. This by no means suggests that user rights are or can be reduced to 'access to information'. Ensuring such rights presupposes a complete transformation of power relations between the different stakeholders and can not be achieved through fragmented and often tokenistic, measures. In this discussion, 'access to information' is understood as an indispensable component of this transformation.

## Involvement in Care Plan

I argued earlier that in a health system dominated by market principles, service users are primarily constructed as consumers. While being a consumer rather than a patient implies the right to choose, this right is rendered meaningless by the lack of information provided to

---

[6] For a full discussion on empowerment strategies in mental health see Barnes & Bowl (2001).

mental health service users. Choice presupposes information on and control over the available options and this is certainly not the case in the Irish system.

The *Annual Report of the Inspector of Mental Hospitals* outlines a number of concerns regarding the Irish mental health system. The issue of information and consultation has been highlighted as particularly deficient for a number of consequent years; however its reoccurrence indicates that there has been no significant progress in this regard. For example, the report for the year 1998 expressed a concern about the adequacy and quality of medical note-taking in a number of mental health services. This related particularly to consultant inputs, and the Inspectorate felt that "in some services the practice of consultants in this regard falls short of what might reasonably be considered good professional practice" (Department of Health and Children, 1999:4). Such practice poses major challenges to basic human rights, in particular related to the deprivation of liberty, as the inspection found that often involuntary patients were re-certified without careful evaluation and that such re-certification was not always recorded in the case notes. The report also stressed that in some cases notes had not been reviewed for over 10 years. Similarly, during the 1999 inspection some of the patients were found to have "had no medical note entries for over four years and ...the case notes of three recently admitted patients had no consultant entry and one of these patients had been in hospital for over two months" (Department of Health and Children, 2000:139). This situation is in breach of the *Guidelines for Good Practice and Quality Assurance in Mental Health Services* recommending that "treatment plans should be discussed with patients... including any medication, clearly recorded in case notes" (Department of Health and Children, 1998:5) and the recommendations of the Inspector of Mental Hospitals that "nursing records should reflect the involvement of patients in planning and making decisions about their own care and treatment, and subsequent evaluation of care plans should include patients' views about progress" (Department of Health and Children, 2001b: 209).

The lack of communication about both diagnosis and treatment plan between service providers and service users has also been a significant finding of two studies on service users' experiences published in 2002. One of these studies is *Pathways*, a service user-led survey of people's experiences of west Galway mental health services in 2000. The *Pathways* report stressed that "71% [of the interviewees] believed their illness was not discussed adequately with them, and 51% said their family was not given an opportunity to discuss the users' illness. Also 67% reported that their treatment programme was not adequately discussed with them, and 67% said this was not discussed with their family....82% said they had no involvement or input into their treatment plan" (Brosnan et al., 2002:43). The second study, *Focusing Minds*, is a review of the Southern Health Board mental health services. This report revealed that one of the main frustrations of service users was not knowing what their illness was. 53% of those interviewed did not know what their diagnosis was and 67% said they got no adequate information about their medication (Southern Health Board, 2002).

These are just some illustrations of the continuous exclusion of people with mental health problems from any meaningful involvement in the management of their condition. The dominant market-led consumerist perspective does not necessarily entail a more democratic approach to service user participation (Croft & Beresford, 1991). On the contrary, it has been argued that "the construction of people with mental illness as consumers encourages the distinction between patients and providers and professionals" (Bolzan et al., 2001: 320). I believe that such patterns of exclusion are as valid indicators of institutional thinking and practice as physical incarceration behind high walls.

## Conclusion

People with mental health problems are a group whose rights are consistently violated in the Irish mental health system. Despite the rhetoric of community care, patterns of institutional thinking and practice still dominate mental health care. Throughout the above discussion, institutionalisation has been re-considered as a form of exclusion that moves beyond the physical incarceration of psychiatric patients behind high walls. Evidence of such exclusion was provided through an examination of the political factors shaping mental health services, the limited nature of service user involvement in mental health care and the narrow view of mental health problems taken by current policy and legislation. It was argued that it is particularly difficult to promote the rights of people with mental health problems in a political context where health increasingly loses its status as a right and becomes a commodity. The institutionalisation of the 'mad' has been a political act of the past. The current reproduction of institutional ideologies within community care is also a political act. Mental health reform in Ireland did not originate in a social demand for a more democratic psychiatry. The hospitals monopolised the debate on mental illness for many years and the medical model still monopolises both hospital and community-based care. Despite the significant development of the Irish service user movement, the dominance of this model has made it difficult for other groups to develop a politically powerful alternative to bio-medical ideology and practice. Within this context, community care developed in an instrumental manner as a collection of services rather than a form of practice providing a broader view of mental distress.

While this discussion has utilised material and evidence from the Irish system, it is important to stress that the questions raised are of universal relevance. The failure to provide inclusive forms of care for people with mental distress is not just an 'Irish problem'. The Irish case, however, can perfectly highlight how institutional thinking and practice can be reproduced through 'reform' policies. To conclude, I wish to evoke the very appropriate description by the Italian psychiatrist Franco Basaglia (1986) of psychiatric institutions as places that simplify and regulate human pain. For a meaningful mental health reform to happen, it is imperative that such forms of institutional thinking and practising will not be reproduced through measures aiming simply to regulate mental distress in the community.

## References

Amnesty International – Irish Section (2003): *Mental Illness, the Neglected Quarter*; Summary Report.

Arora, D. (2001): Reorganisation of Institutional Space State, Market and Public Domain; Institute for Studies in Industrial Development, Delhi and Robarts: Centre for Canadian Studies, York University. Website: (*http:/www.yorku.ca/robarts/archives/chandigarth /pdf/arora_delhi.pdf*)

*Barnes, M./Bowl, R. (2001): Taking over the Asylum*; Basingstoke: Palgrave.

Basaglia, F. (1986): Ideology and Practice on Matters of Mental Health; in: *Tetradia Psychiatrikis* 10, Athens.
Barrington, R. (1987): *Health, Medicine and Politics in Ireland 1900-1970*; Dublin: Institute of Public Administration.
Beresford P./Wallcraft, J. (1997): Psychiatric System Survivors and Emancipatory Research – Issues, Overlaps and Differences; in: Barnes, C. and Mercer, G. (eds,) *Doing Disability Research*, Leeds: The Disability Press.
Brown, V. (2001): Who Cares about Mental Health?; in: *Amnesty*, September 2001.
Bolzam, N. et al. (2001): Creating Identities – Mental Health Consumers to Citizens; in: *Journal of Social Work*, Vol.1, London: Sage Publications.
Brosnan, L. et al. (2002): *Pathways; Experiences of Mental Health Services from a User-Led Perspective*; Galway: Pathways Research Group.
Butler, S. (1987): The Psychiatric Services: Planning for the Future – a Critique; in: *Administration*, 35, 46-48.
Croft, S./Beresford, P. (1991): Learning the Lessons of User Involvement – Implications for Training; in: *Social Work and Social Sciences Review*, 2, 1, 51-60.
Cowen, B., Minister for Health and Children as quoted in the "*Irish Times*", November 1999.
Curry, J. (2003): *Irish Social Services* (4th edition); Dublin: Institute of Public Administration
Daly, A./Walsh, D. (2002): *Irish Psychiatric Hospitals and Units Census 2001*; Dublin: Health Research Board.
Deloitte & Touche (2001): *Audit of the Irish Health System for Value for Money*; Dublin: Department of Health and Children.
Department of Health and Children (2003): *Report of the Inspector of Mental Hospitals for the Year Ending 31st December 2002*; Dublin: Stationery Office.
Department of Health and Children (2001a): *Quality and Fairness: A Health System for You*; Dublin Stationery Office.
Department of Health and Children (2001b): *Report of the Inspector of Mental Hospitals for the Year Ending 31st December 2000*; Dublin: Stationery Office.
Department of Health and Children (2000): *Report of the Inspector of Mental Hospitals for the Year Ending 31st December 1999*; Dublin: Stationery Office.
Department of Health and Children (1999): *Report of the Inspector of Mental Hospitals for the Year Ending 31st December 1998;* Dublin: Stationery Office.
Department of Health and Children (1998): *Guidelines for Good Practice and Quality Assurance in Mental Health Services*; Dublin: Stationery Office.
Department of Health (1994): *Shaping a Healthier Future – A Strategy for Effective Health-Care in the 1990s*; Dublin: Stationery Office.
Department of Health (1984): *Planning for the Future, Report of a Study Group on the Development of the Psychiatric Service*; Dublin Stationery Office.
Expert Group on Mental Health Policy, *www.mentalhealthpolicy.ie* (accessed January 26, 2005).
Fanning, B (2003): The Construction of Irish Social Policy (1953-2003); in: *Administration*, 51, 1-2, 3-18.
Fanning, B. (1999): The Mixed Economy of Welfare; in: G. Kiely, A. O'Donnell, P. Kennedy, S. Quin (eds.) *Irish Social Policy in Context*, Dublin: UCD Press.

Guckian, P. (1998): Mental Health Social Work and the Law in the Republic of Ireland; in: J. Campbell, R. Manktelow, *Mental Health and Social Work in Ireland – Comparative Issues in Policy and Practice,* Aldershot: Ashgate.

Hickey, T./Moran, R./Walsh, D. (2003): *Psychiatric Day Care – An Underused Option?*; Dublin: Health Research Board.

Keogh, F./Roche, A./Walsh, D. (1999): *We Have No Beds...An Enquiry into the Availability and Use of Acute Psychiatric Beds in the Eastern Health Board Region*; Dublin: Health Research Board.

Keys, M. (2002): *Mental Health Act 2001*; Dublin: Round Hall Sweet & Maxwell.

Kuttner, R. (1984): *The Economic Illusion: False Choices between Prosperity and Social Justice*, Boston: Houghton Mifflin.

Leane, M./Sapouna, L. (1998): De-institutionalisation in the Republic of Ireland: A Case for Redefinition?; in: Campbell, J. & Manktelow, R. *Mental Health and Social Work in Ireland – Comparative Issues in Policy and Practice*, Aldershot: Ashgate.

Madianos, M. & Yfantopoulos, J. (1984): *The First Monitoring Report on the Greek Psychiatric Reform: EEC Regulation 815/84*; Brussels: Commission of the European Communities DGV.

Offe, C. (1984): *Contradictions of the Welfare State*; London: Hutchinson.

Pilgrim, D./Rogers, A. (1999): *A Sociology of Mental Illness*, Buckingham: Open University Press.

Powell, F. W. (1992): *The Politics of Irish Social Policy*; New York: Endwin Mellen Press.

Rioux, M. (2002): Disability Citizenship and Rights in a Changing World; in: C. Barnes, M. Oliver, L. Barton, *Disability Studies Today*, Cambridge: Polity Press.

Sapouna, L. (1993): *Community Psychiatry: Confined within the Politics of Progressive Language;* University College Cork: M.Soc.Sc. Thesis (Unpublished).

Southern Health Board (2002): *Focusing Minds – Developing Mental Health Services in Cork and Kerry.*

Speed, E. (2002a): Irish Mental Health Social Movements – A Consideration of Movement Habitus; in: *Irish Journal of Sociology*, 11, 1, 62-80.

Speed, E. (2002b): What Exactly is an Emancipatory Methodology?; *Paper to National Disability Authority Conference on Disability Research*, Dublin: December 2002.

Stefanis, C./Madianos, M./Gilteman, M. (1986): Recent Developments in the Care, Treatment and Rehabilitation of the Chronic Mentally Ill in Greece; in: *Hospital and Community Psychiatry*, 37, 10.

Strutti, C./Rauber, S. (1994): Leros and the Greek Mental Health System; in: *International Journal of Social Psychiatry,* 40, 4.

United Nations Committee on Economic Social and Cultural Rights, 17 May 2002, *UN Doc. No. E/C.12/1/Add.77.*

Yfantopoulos, J. (1994): Economic and Legal Aspects of Mental Health Policies in Greece; in: *International Journal of Social Psychiatry*, 40, 4.

Webb, M. (1993): Closing Mental Hospital Beds – A Re-Appraisal; in: *Psychiatric Nursing*, March 1993, Irish Psychiatric Nursing Association.

Wren, M. (2003): *Unhealthy State – Anatomy of a Sick Society*; Dublin: New Island.

In: Knowledge in Mental Health
Editors: L.Sapouna and P. Herrmann, pp. 101-117
ISBN 1-59454-812-9


*Chapter 7*

# SERVICE USERS AS RESEARCH PARTNERS

***Shulamit Ramon***
Interprofessional Health and Social Studies, School of Community Health and Social Studies, Anglia Polytechnic University, Cambridge, UK

## ABSTRACT

This chapter will look at the increasing involvement of users as research partners in British mental health. The reasons for this radical shift, its promise, the preparation of users to become research partners, and the opportunities and obstacles to this challenge will be discussed. Examples of research projects will be also included.

## INTRODUCTION

This chapter will look at the recent development in engaging users of mental health services as research partners in the UK. It will outline the context and reasons for this development, as well as the value, conceptual and methodological aspects of such an engagement. For me, mental health services have to include health and social care, as I take a mainly psychosocial approach to understanding and intervening in mental health and distress.

The advantages and disadvantages entailed in doing so will be analysed, using examples from studies in which I have been personally involved as well as from those carried out by others.

Presently, users are involved in mental health research in a few other European countries, such as the Netherlands (Romme and Escher, 1993) and Slovenia. However, there the involvement is less systematic, and more likely to involve users who are qualified researchers, rather than users who have not been researchers previously, as in the UK.

## THE CONTEXT

Research has recently become hailed as a central tool for verification of knowledge by British politicians. Each health trust and social services department has to demonstrate its commitment to spreading research awareness and application, as well as encouraging practitioners to engage actively in research.

NICE (National Institute of Clinical Excellence) was established in 1998 by the British (Labour) government with the mandate to take decisions as to which medical interventions can be authorised to be used in the NHS, a multimillion pound market for such interventions. NICE reaches its decisions mainly on the basis of research evidence. When GlaxcoBeechamKlien's flu jab for elderly people was rejected by NICE, the largest pharmaceutical company in the world threatened to quit Britain. NICE has stated that only one type of research evidence is valid, that gathered from Randomised Controlled Trials (RCT), deeming all other research as at best "explorative". Most research in which users participate as researchers would be considered by NICE as invalid.

SCIE (Social Care Institute for Excellence), established in 2001 also by the Labour government, does not have the same clout, perhaps because it is recognised that research in social care cannot claim to have many definitive answers. Indeed, this is often mentioned as a weakness. SCIE's role is to foster and disseminate research in social care. It does involve users in its activities, and applies as research evidence studies based on *interpretative* methodologies.

Thus, user involvement in research is taking place against a background in which there is more than one definition as to what constitutes good research, and hence more than one meaning to knowledge gained from research. Given that the field of mental health is multidisciplinary, this multiplicity of what is meant by research is important.

Traditionally, research has been the occupation of people trained to be researchers in a given discipline, or practitioners who have been given additional training to carry out research. The process of learning to do so requires the completion of at least a master's degree (five years of higher education), and preferably a Ph.D., requiring at least another three years of independent, supervised research work. Therefore to argue that service users, most of whom are unlikely to go through this passage, can be partners to research must seem outrageous to most qualified researchers. While there is a small, yet increasing, number of mental health service users who become qualified researchers, the focus in this chapter is on users who are not qualified researchers and their contribution to mental health research. It will be argued that this shift relates to a specific set of values and to a conceptual framework about the value of specific types of research.

## THE VALUE SET

Being partners to research follows the focus on *inclusionary citizenship*, which did not begin with disabled people but with women and black people in the 1960s. (Chahal, 1999, Fawcett et al, 2000). Its spread to include disabled people, among them those with mental ill health, took place from the 1980s, especially through the Disability Movement (Swain et al, 1993, Barnes and Bowel, 2001). The Disability movement has championed the case that disabled people are *people first*, who have abilities and considerable experience, and whose lessons are largely hidden from professionals and the general public.

In parallel, the emergence of the *Strengths* approach within social work (Rapp, 1992 and 1998), and the *Social Role Valorisation*, first in the field of learning disabilities and then in mental health, (Wolfensberger, 1983, Ramon, 1991) have consolidated the view that service users may have mental health problems and even a mental illness, but this does not negate their abilities, which – if any – should be fostered and put to good use. The current political focus on social inclusion, which pertains also to disabled people, is already in part an outcome of this achievement, as well as of economic considerations (Barry and Hallett, 1998).

This success amounts to a paradigm shift for disabled people in the way they see themselves, the way they approach "able-bodied" people, and the way they would like their social place to be. The stigma attached to any long-term disability, but in particular to mental illness, continues to be part of our daily lives. Nevertheless, there has been a sufficient shift which enables users who can present themselves as capable despite the disability to be more respected than before, and at times also to be given more opportunities to demonstrate their abilities.

Research by leaders of the Disability movement has played an important part in this shift, as did the critical analysis contained in research on disability carried out by others. These leaders have recognised the value and power of research in shaping knowledge, attitudes and practices (Oliver, 1992, Barnes and Mercer, 1997, Beresford and Wallcraft, 1997). A number of them have also concluded that only users should be involved in research on users' issues, an issue looked at below.

Furthermore, the contribution to research by service users was promoted by the valorisation of the personal, subjective experience of disabled people as an important source of knowledge which complements – and/or challenges – the knowledge gained through professional experience within the values set. However, the inclusion of this element does only necessitate the careful and empathic listening to users, rather than their involvement as researchers. This specific component relates to the belief in their equality as contributors to knowledge on their disability, which for some is about their superiority over those without identified disabilities, and for others it concerns mistrust of other people's abilities to accomplish the task as successfully.

The approach taken here comes from the belief that this experience, often associated with stigma, whose bearers are perceived as unproductive members of society and as weaklings, is useful and productive in terms of enabling other users – and the rest of us – to make sense of it through research.

The claim is that user researchers *add value* to what other researchers can offer, and can help to *question* the taken-for-granted epistemological wisdom prevalent in most social science research, let alone natural science research; this wisdom supposes that the neutrality and objectivity of the researcher is a desirable and necessary quality within the researcher-researched relationships and is essential for producing good research.

It also takes further, and differently, the Weberian attempt to understand (Farstein) – where a comparative framework is proposed as the best solution for achieving the understanding of the other from his/her own perspective.

Without negating the usefulness of comparative perspectives as a tool in understanding better the other and oneself, the user researcher is applying her/his *empathic understanding as* a research instrument with which to pinpoint the important research questions as opposed to the less important ones, to make decisions about the suitability of certain methods over others, and to reach out to the research participants. User respondents are also more likely to go beyond their usual boundaries of providing socially desirable responses to qualified researchers when the researcher is perceived as "one of us".

Furthermore, research is not a value-less, neutral, exercise. It can be oppressive, as the power of the researcher is more prominent than that of the participants and s/he can use it as they see fit. Yet it can be also empowering; it is up to the researchers to ensure that it will be so (Everitt et al, 1992, Humphries, 1996). When not tokenistic, user research provides one of the most effective tools for empowering research.

For example, at a presentation of a research project on personality disorder, one of the user researchers came with a broken leg and crutches. She stated that she, normally in the position of being a disliked client, was not ready to give up the unique opportunity to stand up and present the research with her colleagues to a professional audience.

## Ethical Considerations

It is often argued in ethical permission committees, which act as gate-keepers to NHS patients, that it would be harmful to patients to be asked about painful experiences, and if the researcher is a user, it would be damaging for her/him to re-live painful experiences through being a researcher. While these are legitimate concerns, they smack of hypocrisy when used to block the involvement of users in research, rather than to ensure that what is asked and how it is asked are appropriate. These "concerns" reflect the lack of belief that users are strong enough psychologically to be researchers, even if not all of the time. Thus, I was asked in a meeting with such a committee whether I would be present at every interview carried out by user researchers, in case one of them went berserk. This question revealed not only the fear of mental illness as an ever-lurking one, but also a lack of confidence in me as the project manager and in the user researchers. There was concern that the user researchers would not follow the agreed rules of notifying me in the case of feeling unwell in advance of a pre-arranged interview with a user respondent.

An uncomfortable value aspect arises on the rare occasion when a user participant is perceived by a user researcher to be at risk to herself or to others, and has to inform the project managers who will pass on this information to the participant's key worker. Although this is contained in the initial information about the research sent to potential participants, it is experienced by user researchers as a conflict between their caring and controlling functions. Given that they perceive themselves as being only at the receiving end of largely oppressive power relations, it is difficult for them to engage in any controlling capacity in their encounters with other users.

## The Conceptual Base

The move to postmodernity in research paradigms has been an important factor in facilitating the consideration of service users as central partners in research on their disability and on the responses to it from service providers, the service system, policy makers, politicians, and the general public.

As the comparison between NICE and SCIE illustrated, this move is still in the making, and the jury is still out in considering the final verdict.

However, we are witnessing a change from a monolithic and monopolistic model of research to a more fragmented and more open-ended, framework.

On the one hand, we see the continuation of the *positivistic* research paradigm on whose tenets all natural and social scientists were socialised until recently. Most scientists and educated lay people have internalised the belief that positivism offers the "Golden Standard" of scientific research, including detachment from the area and people studied as a necessary, unquestioned element (Popper, 1941, Campbell, 1963, Macdonald and Sheldon, 1992). Within positivism there are clear rules of how to formulate a research question and how to go about finding answers to it, including verifying the value of each answer. The roles of researcher and his/her "*subjects*" is likewise well defined, where the relationships of power are well reflected in the very use of the word "subjects" for the research participants. The latter are expected to be passive in everything but the provision of the information the researcher wishes to find out, which in the case of mental illness ranges from physiological measurements to the most intimate emotional experiences. It is further assumed that the "subject" will offer a reliable version of the truth, and would be willing to do so with a stranger who is treating her/him with respect and detachment. Thus they are treated as objects, rather than as subjects.

Detachment is important within this paradigm, because it is perceived as the hallmark of professional conduct. The knowledge the researcher is looking for is classified as "objective", ensured by the repetition of the methodological tools in the same detached manner with all "subjects".

The paradigm raises many doubts for researchers who do not share these assumptions, and also for stakeholders in the mental health system such as users, carers and professionals, who do not come from a medical background. The doubts include:

- The paradigm negates the impact of the context in which the researchers live and work on their research.
- The process of positivistic inquiry does not enable the views of people most impacted by the phenomenon studied to be heard from their perspective (In Her Own Voice, Gillligan, 1982).
- This elimination begins from the formulation of the research question, and is inherent throughout the different phases of the research process.
- Even when a study attempts to include people's perceptions, these are allowed only through the specific viewpoint of the researcher as to the parameters of the perspectives they may hold. This is reflected in the way questions are phrased, the options allowed for answers, the belief in the value of numerical scales often attached to grading answers, and the type of statistical analysis used, even before reaching the stage of analysing the data and disseminating the conclusions.
- The experimental method, the formulation of a null hypothesis, randomisation, and the equation of significance with statistical probability favoured by the adherents of the positivistic approach are not necessarily enabling researchers to get nearer the

truth, especially in those areas where the meaning attached is both true yet relative (Taylor and Thornicroft, 1996).

Positivistic research is likely to negate the idea that beliefs and values held by the major stakeholders in the area researched need to be an inherent part of the research. In principle, this paradigm negates the fact that beliefs, values and vested interests play a significant part in decision-making concerning the development of any type of science, highlighted by the current debate on genetic research.

The other tradition, which does not negate the value of subjective versions as an inherent part of research, existed before the advance of the positivistic approach, and can be classified as "pre-modern". It has made a comeback with the reintroduction of the *interpretative* paradigm of research as a tool within mainstream social science research since the early 1900s, but especially towards the end of the 20$^{th}$ century with the advent of postmodern discourse (Hughes, 1990, Strauss and Corbin, 1990).

Usually referred to as the "qualitative" approach, the term interpretative is more correct, enabling us to dispose of the assumed, and false, dichotomy between qualitative and quantitative methods in the context of this approach. The interpretative approach takes for granted that people's values, beliefs and own version of reality, and how their version interacts with that of another group of people, is at the core of researching people at the psychosocial level. More fragmented than the positivistic paradigm, the interpretative approach legitimises asking a variety of questions and using equally a variety of methods for their exploration. This does not mean lack of rigour, which is to be found in the internal consistency of the overarching methodology. There are differences between grounded theory, the narrative approach and the constructivist model, but these models also share the attempt to explore beyond observed phenomenon into meanings, and the importance of meanings in determining social and personal realities. They also share the recognition that the research and the researchers' context influences what will be asked and how it will be researched, as well as what will happen to the findings. Researchers therefore need to acknowledge their values (biases) as well as those of the research participants. "Subjects" become *participants* in the interpretative paradigm in recognition of their active contribution to shaping the research.

However, most of the existing interpretative research continues to be carried out largely by qualified researchers, and only a minority has moved to engage participants as researchers.

Action research has been the major research methodology to move to such a participation (Hart and Bond, 1995, Winter and Munn-Giddings, 2000). The co-existence of research and action and the inter-dependence of researchers and participants in this methodology created a welcoming environment for such experimentation. Participants tended to be practitioners and/or ordinary people, living in a given neighbourhood, who wanted to bring about a desired change there. Paolo Friere's (1972) shared work/educational research with peasants in Latin America in the 1960s began this trend.

The history of competing research paradigms can be as nasty as that of commercial competitions today, even if more polite in expression (Kuhn, 1970). It remains to be seen whether different approaches to thinking about and doing research will be allowed to coexist (which would signify the victory of postmodernism) or whether only one paradigm will be permitted (signifying the re-emergence of modernity).

This state of affairs is reflected, for example, in the fact that we have not yet reached the stage in which interpretative research is viewed as equal in scientific power to that of the positivistic paradigm within mainstream health care research, as it is perceived to be an "exploratory" tool which, on its own, does not enable conclusive answers to the research questions to be reached. Ethics committees, which rightly have to sanction permission to carry out research with service users, continue to be staffed by professionals who are both suspicious of the interpretative approach and ignorant of it.

*Involving users as researchers* has meant taking one – bold – further step in the direction of engaging participants as researchers by emphasising the value of the contribution of service users as active researchers *when they are not professionally qualified as researchers, but when they are trained to undertake specific research tasks and participate in the research process as a whole.*

Research is defined here operationally as the systematic study of an issue focused upon, often using more than one method in the search for more comprehensive answers, and an analysis of these new attempts at providing answers.

## Training and Supporting Service Users as Researchers

Can the research be of good quality if the researchers are not formally qualified? There are convincing examples which demonstrate that it is possible to carry out good quality research when not all, or even most of the researchers have had research experience (Castillo, 2002, Barratt et al, 1999). A crucial factor in the success or failure of user research projects is the training on offer.

Purtell et al (2003) outline how they went about stimulating interest in research while de-mystifying it, attempting to create a culture of research which would promote the status of evidence-based practice for both users and practitioners. A tool for *community capacity* building, the project has constructed a number of stimulating steps to further these objectives.

Castillo (2002) describes how users with personality disorder have been trained over a period of three months to conduct in-depth interviews with other users who have the same attributed diagnostic category. Working with a group used to telling and writing stories and poems about their experiences, applying mainly interactive methods such as role play, pair exercises, bringing in a user group who has already carried out research to discuss their experience, engaging the group in creating the interview schedule, have all contributed to enabling the members of the group to be reliable interviewers on an agreed schedule. This was accompanied during the training period and the actual interviewing stage by informal support and de-briefing, offered by the project manager. Although nearly everyone in the group had gone through a personal crisis while the research project was in progress, this type of support enabled the user researchers to come back to the group and to interviewing after such a crisis. One of them stated that to be able to come back was an incentive for her to recover earlier than on previous occasions. It meant also that rules for notifying the project manager of being unable to interview had to be very clear, and had to be adhered to – which they were.

In the user-run project described by Barratt et al (1999), the research adviser provided the user researchers with summaries of training sessions between sessions, gave each of them a task to perform between meetings, and began the process by asking them to tell their story to one other user in the group.

Payne (2003) offers an example of how a university module, focused on reflective writings, can facilitate making sense of one's experience as a service user, and how the presence of professionals does not have to be intimidating and can be supportive. From this stand-alone module, Payne went to do a master's degree in action research, and a dissertation research on carers.

The training has to achieve seemingly incompatible objectives. It has to *de-mystify* research and de-jargonise its language, while at the same time enabling people to have a good enough understanding of its internal logic and its application to the issues investigated. It also has to enthuse participants to the point that they wish to remain throughout the whole process, which inevitably has some less interesting or/and uncomfortable elements. While they may not posses research skills from the outset, they should be encouraged to contribute actively with their considerable experience and relevant generic skills they often bring, such as being good listeners, respectful and able to demonstrate empathy. Trainees need to feel they are making progress individually and as a group early on, supported when stuck, and praised for their achievements. How to enable participants to decline an interview if they change their mind or are flooded by the impact of past experience is an important skill to be practised side by side with de-briefing techniques for the user researchers themselves. It is essential to have a lot of experiential opportunities, realistic role-play, putting oneself in the shoes/skin of others, and learning from other user researchers. The training is thus a central stage of the research, in which decisions are reached and implemented as to the research questions and methodology.

The training period can, and should be, used for confidence and trust-building, for providing detailed and accurate information about the various aspects of the research including pay, and for raising doubts and questions. The principles of adult learning, now re-discovered on many nursing and social work qualifying courses, also apply to this case.

The training process also provides a "cooling-off" period in which users who find that this is not what they wish to – or can effectively – do, can leave without losing face. It is more tricky – and requires considerable tact – for the training co-ordinators to encourage some users to leave, yet it may be necessary instead of setting them to fail, and/or letting them fail the research participants.

The inclusion of *practitioners* as active research partners needs a training element too. In many ways, practitioners feel as alienated from research as users, as they do not usually have a say in either the formulation of the research questions or the research methodology.

In a project conducted by Magjlijlic (2003) on users', practitioners' and students' views on social work education in Cambridge and Sarajevo, all the participants first had a long meeting with the project manager to clarify what the project was about, their commitment and support structure, and they had tasks to perform between meetings. Magjlijlic's co-chair for the meetings was a mental health service user.

## The Issue of Power

Power emerges as a key issue within user research. User research has been developed as a method of creating new knowledge, hitherto hidden and often described as invalid by professionals. Knowledge itself is powerful in providing a way to make sense, give meaning, and predict reality.

In addition, it has the potential to lead to a shift in the existing knowledge established by professionals by offering a new way of looking at what has been taken for granted by them, often offering an alternative *critical* perspective. Thus it can be a powerful tool with which to challenge professional knowledge and the power it carries.

Acquiring the ability to carry out research either alongside professional researchers or on a par with them is adding competencies, conferring a socially desirable status on service users as they undertake a socially valued role. This can *empower* users to be more equal in power to non-labelled citizens.

Power is also an issue in *paying* users for their work in research, as payment symbolises recognition for socially valued work, in this case to people most of whom would be living on benefits and hence would be poor. It is not easy to resolve the issue of this pay having to fall within the limits on earnings for people on benefits. Pay has to be thought through in advance, including the waiting time between carrying out a research task and being paid for it.

Thus, a number of *positive aspects* of power (Rees, 1991) come to the fore in user research, so unlike the experience of being a service user, largely overburdened by the negative connotation of power.

Power is also an issue in taking into account the context of user research, where age, class, ethnicity, and gender play a part in determining who is likely to become and remain a service user, as well as in whether specific types of interventions will be of help or hindrance to users.

Finally, power is an issue in the relationships between user researchers and professional researchers when collaborative work is aimed at. As the professional researcher usually comes with greater knowledge and skills of the research process, while the user researcher comes with considerable experiential knowledge, the risk of the former controlling the latter should not be underestimated, as methodological knowledge and skills continue to be essential for building up the ability of users to be researchers. Often, users come lacking confidence in their abilities to do research and having doubts as to the usefulness of engaging in anything using complicated jargon and portrayed as "academic", while at the same time being attracted to it. Some come with a niggling suspicion as to why professional researchers would wish to work with them, if not for the purpose of exploiting their experience for the purpose of glorifying the professional researcher.

Professional researchers may come with a sense of superiority and confidence, either unsure as to whether users can master the skills required for meeting the research tasks, or else expecting users to be as good as themselves in a very short time. The niggling doubts and low self-esteem of many highly intelligent users, at times manifesting themselves in a reluctance to take decisions or in taking "too much" time over it, come as an unwelcome surprise to professional researchers.

Not coming from the research world, users may not appreciate the fact that most professional researchers who are keen to work in partnership with users are, to an extent, risking their credibility as researchers in the eyes of the majority of their colleagues. They are also demonstrating a readiness to take a risk by opting for a much less charted route of research, i.e. working with non-professional researchers, on the ups and downs of a participatory path.

In the funding structure, often the professional researcher will be given responsibility for the funding, thus accentuating the sense of this person being more powerful than the user researcher.

In extreme situations, this may feel like a clash of two cultures. In less extreme instances, it is about taking pains to learn about and from each other within a framework which is structured to be user-led from the very beginning. The Joseph Rowntree Foundation has recently announced that its disability research sector will be guided by a user group from the Shaping Our Lives social care project; hopefully this is an attempt to ensure that the research agenda is more *user-led*.

This scenario has led a number of users to not engage in research in the first place, or to want to do it on their own, either by hiring a "tamed" researcher to act as a consultant or by attempting to "reinvent the wheels" of research. Yet in my view all three are missed opportunities, as each partner has a lot to offer to the other. Thus it is the *quality of the partnership* which will determine if any given project is indeed user-led or not.

It is crucial that user-led research will be of good quality, given that:

a. If the aim is to ultimately contribute to improving users' lives, it is not worth investing in poor quality research.
b. There is an expectation that user research will fail and be exposed as poor research by a large number of those who doubt the validity of involving them in the first place.

Good quality user research needs good professional knowledge of research, as much as the experiential knowledge brought in by the users.

As the definition of being a user is wide-ranging and subjective, and a number of the professional researchers may have been service users intermittently, we are trading in "muddy waters" here when arguing that anyone who is not defining herself/himself as a user cannot be a valued contributor to user-led research. The multiplicity of identities ascribed to the authors of this book, typical of postmodernity, also highlights this point. Hence, within the collaborative relationships, it is necessary to find ways which enable not merely the co-existence of users and professional researchers, but the genuine participation of both as equal contributors to a shared endeavour. This is possible, if not easy or always comfortable. For example, in Butler's (2003) project on multi-media autobiographies of women with mental ill health problems, the project manager (Butler) participated in the same way as any other woman participant-researcher in exploring her own autobiography.

I admit to being weary of highly formalised procedures with which to anchor good partnerships between user researchers and professional researchers, as these can become too rigid and are unlikely ever to encapsulate all eventualities. However, I would like to emphasise the need for an agreed framework from which to work on the partnership itself.

In principle, there is also a place for non-users to research users, as much as for users to research non-users, if multi-perspectives are the objective we are aiming at (Harris and Paylor, 1999). However, this is not the focus of this book.

User research is thus defined here as one in which users are equal partners to the major decisions taken about the research and the whole research process, while the research focus is driven by users' concerns. This operational definition differs from the more formal "user-controlled" (Beresford and Wallcraft, 1997, Evans and Fisher, 1998), and takes its cue from the concept of Prosumers, coined by Monica Savio (Savio, 2000) in her attempt to describe and analyse the role of users in a welfare organisation. In this role, they are producers of relationships, interactions, outcomes and processes, just as much as consumers of these parameters produced by others, such as practitioners, professional researchers and research participants.

## Representation

Purtell, Baxter and Mitchell (2003) questioned accusatorily whether the users interested in research do indeed represent all users in an area, or of a disability. This is unlikely to be the case as people interested in research, let alone those who become engaged in it, tend to be a minority in a population which credits systematic investigation as having more meaning than sporadic individual experiences. It is unclear why user researchers are expected to be more representative of either users or researchers than researchers are normally.

However, there is a clear need to ensure the best available representation of the *diversity* of the population studied in any research about people, groups and populations, for the purpose of being able to reach more generalised meanings and, at times, recommendations.

## Dissemination

The importance of this phase of research is more emphasised today than used to be the case, in recognition of the alarming lack of knowledge about relevant, specific research projects and the application of their findings by agencies that should know better, by practitioners, and at times by policy makers. Indeed, what is the point of investing in research if its lessons are not learned?

In an attempt to remedy this sorry state of affairs, the reasons for which have been outlined in the introduction to this book, the government, urged by the NISW (National Institute of Social Work), has recently established SCIE (Social Care for Information Excellence) as a disseminating body for social care, while NICE has similar, and additional responsibilities for health care. As already mentioned, NICE is expected to determine the value of research and of specific interventions such as medication.

Presumably, the government is accepting that existing social care evidence is not of a calibre sufficient to enable us to pass this type of judgement. Those sceptical of the validity of the type of evidence favoured by NICE – invariably of positivistic origin – would argue that this belief needs to be extended to the health sphere also. Most current user research would only merit to be considered as *"grey"* evidence, terminology used in official publications of research bids by the Department of Health. In other words, it is inferior in quality to research carried out without users' active participation.

At the same time, the emphasis on much wider dissemination of research in both health and social care should be welcomed, as it has the potential to open up this hitherto neglected area to all those front-line workers and managers, users and carers, who are thus far uninitiated into the appreciation and use of research, let alone into participating in and conducting it.

The NHS also initiated Consumers in NHS Research in 1999 (re-named INVOLVE in 2003), which as from 2002 has also included social care. This organisation focuses on informing users -and anyone else on the mailing list – of research activities focused on user issues, via a newsletter and workshops. Thus far the information provided has depended on information received from those who have answered the fairly long questionnaire which the organisation sends by post. The systematic provision of knowledge, skills and debate on problematic issues in research for users is still not happening. The organisation has just been merged with the Cancer Development Network and has allied itself with the social care research arm of York University. Are these signs of a better, more inclusive future for user research or for a narrower one, both in terms of category of disability and research framework? Time will tell.

The Toronto group aims at promoting empowering research in health and social care. It is a UK national group of mainly social care researchers and users interested in research; the name of the Canadian city reflects the fact that it was established by British researchers who met at a conference on empowerment in Toronto.

The Mental Health Foundation has established a network of user researchers in this field, based on its activities in this field. It prefers a user-only model.

The research network described by Purtell, Baxter and Mitchell (2003) and referred to above, and the one initiated by the department of social work at Birmingham University, are examples of regional and local networks.

If anything, these recent developments accentuate the urgent need to disseminate user research to all stakeholder groups, beginning with other users but also aiming to reach carers, practitioners, managers, researchers, policy makers and politicians. Local and national conferences provide many such opportunities. However, they require funding and organisation, as well as preparing user researchers unused to public presentations; it can be a scary experience on the first few occasions.

It is important for user researchers to have the skills required for dissemination, such as public speaking, writing, and/or use of multimedia methods, as well as in-built opportunities for using these skills within each project, be it at the local, regional, national or international level. Paying for the expenses incurred through dissemination (e.g. travelling expenses, work on preparing a newsletter or a CD-Rom) needs to be taken care of in advance to ensure the involvement of user researchers in dissemination. In addition to spreading the information about a specific project and its message, the engagement in dissemination offers the user researcher opportunities for further learning, for, for engaging in dialogues with other stakeholders in research, for attaining greater awareness of what impacts on research, and for networking.

The more difficult presentations are those given to local professionals, as often user research is insufficiently positive from the users' perspectives regarding their contributions. In the research project on personality disorder (Ramon, Castillo and Morant, 2001) there was a total silence when it was presented to local professionals, in contrast to the applause and many questions when presented at the National Institute of Social Work.

What do user researchers do when the project in which they have participated finishes? This phase may feel like an anti-climax, like being abandoned. Networking in advance can prevent this from happening, as can laying the foundations for further joint activity resulting from the project, such as another dissemination step in the near future.

For some user researchers, participation in a research project provides the incentive to engage in further studies, either about research or other issues. Others may move in the direction of becoming more active around user issues. Most user researchers, but not all, comment on the positive sense of achievement in mastering the research task, in communicating with the research participants, in informing professionals about vital yet hitherto missing aspects of user experience and in making them listen respectfully to users. All of these highlight the social role valorisation aspect of this activity, its empowering value, and its place in de-stigmatising service users.

The *capacity building* and the enhancement of *human and social capital* that are embedded in enabling users to act as researchers could – and should – be further utilised by health and social care agencies in their locality in building a local network of user researchers to be re-employed in future projects. The same applies to the contribution to our knowledge brought about by user research.

## THE CONTRIBUTION OF RESEARCH INVOLVING USERS TO KNOWLEDGE IN MENTAL HEALTH

The knowledge we have gained thus far from user-led research and research in which users are actively involved pertains to research methodology, views about mental illness and distress, views about legislation and policy implementation, professional responses, and the experience of being researchers.

### Research Methodology

User respondents are more comfortable with open-ended questions and qualitative methods. User researchers often prefer more structured tools, either because they think this is more scientific, or because it feels easier to administer and to interpret.

Some user researchers who have experienced a multimedia approach to researching their biography felt very positive about this method (Butler, 2003). Payne (2003) highlights the usefulness of disciplined self-reflection as a method, while Maglijlic illustrates the value of co-operative inquiry (2003) and Schafer (2003) has demonstrated the usefulness of questionnaires and quantitative analysis.

### Views about Mental Illness and Distress

Unlike medical knowledge, users view their experiences of mental illness and distress as clearly related to negative life events and rooted in interpersonal relations. Therefore, they prefer psychosocial approaches and interventions to the medical model. This should not be read as a negation of the value of any medical intervention, but rather against its monopoly in many mental health facilities to the exclusion of other approaches. While some are content with the notion that they have an illness that can be also treated medically, the majority feel that their view is often negated by mental health professionals (Rogers, Pilgrim and Lacey, 1993).

In the case of personality disorder, user research has highlighted the doubts about the validity of the diagnostic category (Castillo, 2002). Castillo proposed taking into account the traumatic nature of the experiences of most of those to whom this diagnosis is attributed. This should lead to a revised name and diagnosis.

## Users Think that Positive Policy Initiatives are Often Left Unimplemented

For example, user researchers have highlighted the fact that most users do not see their care plan, even though the policy and its regulations require that they see it before it is agreed, and that they will be given a copy of it to keep (Rose, 2000). They would like to have a choice in which services to use and the ability to decide how to use resources, such as funding and housing, which are allocated to them.

Mental health legislation is perceived to be primarily coercive, aimed at removing people rather than providing them with what they need. While users often accept that they need to be away from the place in which they experience their problems, most of them do not see hospitalisation as an adequate alternative. The revised Mental Health Bill presented last year was rejected by both users and carers (and most professionals) because of the punitive approach to people with personality disorder, as the law proposed their preventive detention if they have a negative reputation.

## Views about Services and Service Providers

Many users are very unhappy about the impersonal approach they meet in admission wards; they feel neglected and unheard by staff, find the activities boring, and at times find the other patients dangerous and disruptive. They do not think the staff do enough to stop bullying and violent incidences on the ward (Secker & Harding, 2002).

Community mental health centres are perceived in a more positive light, as are specialised projects on employment and advocacy.

Users are making it clear that they would like to have more personalised attention from staff, more listening and empathy, better continuity of staff, and to be treated as people rather than as patients.

Services which offer a personalised approach and focus on helping clients to sort out the problems they wish to resolve in an informal way are praised by clients, (as well as by key workers and professional colleagues from the referring statutory agencies (Ramon, 2003b).

## The Experience of being Researchers

Relatively little has been explored about this aspect of knowledge, as the involvement of users in research is relatively new and is limited to a small number of people, however articulate they may be.

Most users who participated as researchers have found the experience positive and empowering. A few were unhappy about what they considered to be the tokenistic nature of their involvement (i.e. where only one user participated, s/he was given the least important task).

The critique inherent in the users' views amounts to stating that being treated as a human being is more important for them than professional expertise, and that often the service fails in providing that human quality. This could be dismissed as the view of people who do not understand the value of professional responses, or as a valid critique of medicalised professionalism.

## Summary

In conclusion, I would hope that the case for the importance of engaging users as researchers has been made convincingly above.

Users, practitioners, researchers, policy makers and politicians have compelling reasons to benefit from this focus as a method which adds truth, power, and validity to those to whom it has been hitherto denied. Users benefit from the participation in research both as researchers and as respondents, even if both groups cannot ensure that participative research findings will be taken with the seriousness they deserve.

Furthermore, the method demonstrates the abilities that users have, and the content is often illuminating in making us re-consider what has been taken up to now as the only truth (for a detailed discussion of the benefits of user-led research to the different stakeholders see Ramon, 2003, chapter 1).

When the findings from user-focused research are taken seriously, they also have the potential to radicalise conceptual and intervention frameworks.

## References

Barnes, C./Mercer, G. (eds.) (1997): *Doing Disability Research*; Leeds: The Disability Press.

Barnes, M./Bowl, R. (2001): *Taking Over the Asylum – Empowerment and Mental Health*; Basingstoke: Palgrave.

Barratt, M./Morgan, C./Knight, T./Smith, S./Maglajlic, R. (1999): *Lifecraft Evaluation;* Cambridge: Anglia Polytechnic University.

Barry, M./Hallett, C. (eds.) (1998): *Social Exclusion and Social Work – Issues of Theory, Policy and Practice*; Lyme Regis, Russell House Publishing.

Beresford, P./Wallcraft, J. (1997): Psychiatric System Survivors and Emancipatory Research – Issues, Overlaps and Differences; in: C. Barnes, G. Mercer, (eds.) *Doing Disability Research*, Leeds: The Disability Press.

Butler, A. (2003): Whose Life is it Anyway? Creative Autobiography with Service Users; in: S. Ramon, (ed.) *Users Researching Health and Social Care – An Empowering Agenda?*, Birmingham: Venture Press.

Castillo, H. (2002): *Personality Disorder – Temperament or Trauma?* London: Jessica Kingsley, Forensic Focus 23.

Chahal, K. (1999): Researching Ethnicity – Experiences and Concerns; in: B. Broad, (ed.) *The Politics of Social Work Research and Evaluation*, Birmingham: Venture Press.

Campbell, D. (1963): *Experimental and Quasi-experimental Designs for Research*; Chicago: Rand and McNally.

Evans, C./Fisher, M. (1998): User Controlled Research and Empowerment; in: W. Shera, Wells, L. (eds.) *Empowerment Practice in Social Work – Developing Richer Conceptual Foundations*, Toronto, Canadian Scholars Press.

Everitt, A./Hardiker, P./Littlewood, J./Mullender, A. (1992): *Applied Research for Better Practice*; Basingstoke: Macmillan.

Fawcett, B./Featherstone, B./Fook, J./Rossiter, A. (eds.) (2000): *Practice and Research in Social Work – Postmodern Feminist Perspectives*; London: Routledge.

Friere, P. (1972): *Pedagogy of the Oppressed;* Harmondsworth: Penguin Books.

Harris, J./Paylor, I. (1999): The Politics of Difference – Researching those Dissimilar from the Self; in: B. Broad, (ed.) *The Politics of Social Work Research and Evaluation*, Birmingham: Venture Press.

Hart, E./Bond. M. (1995): *Action Research in Health and Social Care*; The Open University, Milton Keynes.

Hughes, J. (1990): *The Philosophy of Social Research*; London: Longman.

Humphries, B. (ed.) (1996): *Critical Perspectives on Empowerment*; Birmingham; Venture Press.

Kuhn, T. (1970): *The Structure of Scientific Revolutions*; (2nd edition), Chicago: University of Chicago Press.

Macdonald, G.M./Sheldon, B. (1992): Contemporary Studies of the Effectiveness of Social Work; in: *British Journal of Social Work*, 22, 6, 615-643.

Maglijlic, R. (2003): *Co-Operative Inquiry in Cambridge and Sarajevo – Towards a Critical Understanding of Social Work Education*; in: S. Ramon, op.cit., 111-122.

Oliver, M. (1992): Changing the Social Relations of Research Production? in: *Disability, Handicap and Society*, 7, 2, 101-113.

Oliver, M. (1996): *Understanding Disability – From Theory to Practice*; Basingstoke: Macmillan.

Payne, J. (2003): *Researching Oneself Through Reflective Writing;* in: S. Ramon, op. cit., 27-34.

Popper, C. (1941): *The Logic of Scientific Discovery*; London: Heinemann.

Purtell, Mitchell (2003): *Doing Research Together – The Forum for Collaboration with Users in Research at Exeter University*; in: S. Ramon, op. cit, 133-141.

Ramon, S./Castillo, H./Morant, N. (2001): Experiencing Personality Disorder: A participatory Research Project; in: *The International Journal of Psychiatry*, 47, 4, 1-15.

Ramon, S. (ed.) (1991): *Beyond Community Care – Normalisation and Integration Work;* Basingstoke: Mind Macmillan.

Ramon, S. (ed.) (2003a): *Users Researching Health and Social Care: An Empowering Agenda?* Birmingham: Venture Press.

Ramon, S. (2003b): *An Evaluation of four Turning Point Projects*; Cambridge: Anglia Polytechnic University.

Rees, S. (1991): *Achieving Power*; London: Allen Lane.

Rogers, A./Pilgrim, D./Lacey, R. (1993): *Experiencing Psychiatry – Users' Views of Services;* Basingstoke: Mind Macmillan.

Romme, M., Escher, S. (1993): *Accepting Voices*; London: Mind Publications.
Rose, D. (1999): Do It Yourselves; in: *Mental Health Care*, 2,5, 174-177.
Savio, M. (2000): *The Dynamics of Management (unpublished paper),* Moscow and Irkutsk, Tempus Programme Health Management of Russian Children and Maternity Services.
Secker, J./Harding, C. (2002): African and African Caribbean Users' Perceptions of Inpatient Services; in: *Journal of Psychiatric and Mental Health Nursing*, 9,2, 161-168.
Schafer, T. (2003): *Researching User Empowerment in Practice – Lessons from the Field*; in: S. Ramon, S. op.cit.
Strauss, A./Corbin, J. (1990): *Basics of Qualitative Research – Grounded Theory Procedures and Techniques*; London: Sage.
Swain, J./Finklestein, V./French, S./Oliver, M. (eds.) (1993): *Disabling Barriers – Enabling Environments;* London: Sage.
Taylor, R., Thornicroft, G. (1996): Uses and Limits of Randomised Controlled Trials in Mental Health Service Research; in: M. Tansella, G. Thornicroft, (eds.) *Mental Health Outcomes Measures*, Berlin: Springer.
Thyer, B. (1993): Social Work Theory and Practice Research – An approach of Logical Positivism; in: *Social Work and Social Science Review*, 4,1, 5-26.
Winter, R./Munn-Giddings, C. (2001): *A handbook for Action Research in Health and Social Care*, London. Routledge.
Wolfensberger, W. (1983): *Social Role Valorisation: A Proposed New Term for the Principle of Normalisation; in: Mental Retardation*, 21, 234-239, Toronto.

In: Knowledge in Mental Health
Editors: L.Sapouna and P. Herrmann, pp. 119-142
ISBN 1-59454-812-9


*Chapter 8*

# COMPARING MENTAL HEALTH SERVICES ACROSS EUROPE – FROM EVALUATION TO QUALITY ASSURANCE

*Miguel Xavier*
The Medical School, Lisbon New University, Portugal

## ABSTRACT

In the last decade, mental health service evaluation has become an area of increasing interest, for three main reasons: changes in patterns of care delivery, shortage of resources, and user/family pressure, with a great focus on concepts like equity, effectiveness and quality.

Despite this interest, mental health service evaluation is not a simple process: on the contrary, the lack of knowledge about the aetiology of mental health, as well as the difficulty of setting standards, criteria and indicators for mental health care, illustrate clearly the problems that carers and researchers have to face in order to achieve good quality patterns of health care delivery.

In this chapter, the impact of the construct of *quality* upon mental health services evaluation is analysed, focusing on general methodological issues such as indicators selection (e.g., structure, process, outcome) and technical proceedings.

The consensual insufficiency of the classical evaluation models acknowledged by the author led him to outline, both conceptually and methodologically, a set of different constructs which have been raised to a central place in mental health services evaluation: needs assessment, satisfaction, quality of life and family burden.

To illustrate this, the author reports on a multicentric study focusing on the comparison between Northern vs. Southern Europe, concerning needs for care status, delivery of care and availability of community-based treatment and community resources.

## INTRODUCTION

Despite the fact that it is three decades behind other medical fields (Fauman, 1989), over the last few years three factors have been causing the subject of care quality assessment to take on a growing importance in the planning and organisation of psychiatric and mental health services.

The first of the three is linked to the far-reaching change in psychiatric assistance systems that has been taking place in western countries since the second half of the 20th century, a change that we generically know by the name "deinstitutionalisation" (Bachrach, 1996).

In fact, the recognition of the inadequacies of asylum-based models on the one hand and the ideological criticism of the negative repercussions of prolonged hospitalisation (Barton, 1959;Goffman, 1961;Wing, 1970) on the other undeniably contributed to the progressive replacement of the stigmatised old organisational structures by heterogeneous, decentralised care-provision systems – in other words, to the advent of community psychiatry.

In this new context, in which the multiplicity of measures and therapeutic approaches came to be seen as one of the central paradigms, the need to study the success of the transformations that had been put into place naturally led to the institution of care evaluation, not only as a technical imperative but also as an ethical one.

The second concerns the impact of restrictive factors of an economic nature in a system in which the mismatch between the population's needs and the available resources is becoming greater and greater, and in which mental health is not always furnished with a budget that corresponds to its epidemiological and clinical importance (WHO, 2001).

In many cases, this aspect of things is getting worse due to the persistence of a profound asymmetry between the budgets of hospitals and those of community structures (Caldas de Almeida, 1996; Burti, 1997; Knapp, 1997).

Given that reallocating resources is one of the more viable alternatives for rectifying these asymmetries, it is not difficult to see how important a role the assessment of the various health services' effectiveness has been playing in this matter in a number of countries in the western world (Häfner, 1996; Jenkins, 1997; Goldberg, 1997; Sartorius, 1997).

The third and last factor involves the growing weight that public opinion movements have been acquiring in the discussions about the process of providing care in mental health services. Made up of patients and their families, user associations base their demands on the integral fulfilment of a series of prerogatives, which include facilitated access to specialist services, obtaining good quality care and prior information about the characteristics of the different therapeutic methods, and calls to governments to draw up specific legislation designed to protect the rights of patients with psychiatric disturbances and to implement assessment systems.

As a direct consequence of these factors, an ever-growing number of authors have been pointing to evaluation as a crucial step towards the development of psychiatric assistance that is based on solid scientific criteria, in that is makes it possible to test rigorously both the efficacy of therapeutic programmes and the degree to which the ethical prerequisites (fairness, the accessibility and continuity of care, etc.) that are involved in the context of the provision of care in today's societies are fulfilled (Caldas de Almeida,1995; Wing, 1996; Jenkins, 1997; Tansella,1997).

However, despite the attention which it has been receiving in scientific circles and which is reflected in the exponential increase in papers in the specialist press, the truth is that far from being sufficiently well delimited in its details, quality assessment continues to prove a fertile ground for problems, obstacles and contradictions. Most of these problems arise as much in the conceptual and methodological fields as they do in the operational one (Brugha, 1996), and the scientific validity of the process itself depends on a resolution of these problems.

## Applying the Concept of Quality to Mental Health Service Evaluation

Healthcare quality may be defined as "... the degree in which healthcare services enhance the probability of occurrence of certain desired results for the individual, in accordance with the most current principles and technical knowledge" (Lohr, 1992: 124).

This definition goes hand in hand with two instrumental concepts of the utmost importance: 1. *Quality evaluation*, which corresponds to the assessment of the degree of healthcare quality, according to certain standards and criteria, and 2. *Quality assurance*, a set of procedures aiming to develop and maintain high standards of quality in healthcare provision, through monitoring.

Quality is something that does not possess a physical existence and consequently cannot be directly quantified. As a result, if we are to measure the quality of care it is first of all necessary to define clearly what dimensions must be assessed. Inasmuch as the dimensions condition the value judgement that is used to gauge the overall quality of care, they are normally known as *partial components of quality*.

There are a number of partial components specified in literature (Dickens, 1994), such as:

- *Accessibility* – the possibility of a consumer obtaining the services he or she needs at a time and place where and when they are needed, in sufficient amounts and at reasonable cost (or free). The three measurable dimensions are personal accessibility, comprehensiveness of services and quantitative adequacy.
- *Technical quality* – professional competence, personal acceptability and qualitative adequacy.
- *Continuity* – the treatment of a consumer as a whole person in an integrated way under the guidance of a central source of care. Measurable aspects include person-centred care, the existence of a central source of care and co-ordination of services.
- *Efficiency* – the relationship between the impact of the service and its costs. Measurable components include the existence of equitable financing, adequate compensation for negligence and efficient administration and management.
- *Appropriateness* – the service or procedure is what the person actually needs.
- *User quality* – what consumers want from the service, both individually and as a population.
- *Equity* – a fair share is available for the whole population.

- *Acceptability* – services are provided so as to satisfy the health expectations of users, providers and the community.
- *Management quality* – the most efficient and productive use of resources to meet users' needs within limits set by higher authorities.

The next step is to represent these (and other) dimensions by numeric variables – also known as indicators – that are capable of being processed using quantitative methods. Examples of the many types of indicator include mortality rates, average wait for in-patient admission, number of re-admissions, waiting time for a doctor's appointment, the number of professionals in a given healthcare unit and their different technical skills, and user and staff satisfaction.

Under ideal circumstances, indicators should possess the same characteristics as statistical measurements, i.e. they should measure exactly that which they are supposed to (validity), give the same results when measured under similar conditions but using different techniques (reliability), detect changes, however small they may be (sensitivity), and measure variations only within the context of the predefined criteria (specificity).

It is obviously impossible to achieve these objectives fully, so indicators should essentially be seen as approximate measurements of a given reality and never as the reality itself. However, if they are only analysed on the basis of their absolute value, indicators may not be much use in practice, given that, as we said earlier, there can be no assessment without comparison. So, before we actually assess, we must define a reference system composed of given criteria and standards, which will serve as a basis for comparison against which the figures for each indicator under study can be set.

When it comes to assessing quality, the term *criterion* means a norm that defines the way a given activity or programme is executed and makes it uniform. Examples include the reference doses used in vaccines, or, in the psychiatric field, the diagnostic systems used in the international classifications (e.g. ICD10, DSM-IV).

*Standards* are pre-established values that determine whether or not a criterion is being complied with within the quality limits that have been agreed as acceptable. For example, in the case of a criterion which stipulates that the ideal average length of stay for in-patient episodes should be less than thirty days, and if we consider and stipulate in advance that this deadline should not be exceeded in 90% of situations, it is precisely this threshold that constitutes the standard.

Criteria and standards are thus the general guidelines that should underlie a health service's work, if it is to guarantee the provision of care of the highest quality.

*To put it simply, the care quality assessment process is based on the correct identification of the aspects that are to be assessed, the definition of the indicators that represent those aspects and the creation in advance of a set of reference criteria and standards.*

Taking Donabedian's (1980) seminal work as a starting point, it is customary to define and characterise healthcare indicators on the basis of three primary issues: structure, process and outcomes.

By *structure* we mean the set of human, financial, material, technical and organisational resources on which a health service's activities/programmes rest (table 1). In general terms, these elements are relatively stable and not especially difficult to quantify – something that on the face of it could help us to see them as a good way to correlate the quality of care. Nevertheless, they only provide an approximate idea of quality, and even then only to the extent that they establish a physical context for the provision of care, and they have therefore progressively been relegated to a secondary role.

**Table 1. Structure Indicators (adap. WHO, 1991a)**

1. **Physical environment**
   a. Space.
   b. Space distribution for patients, relatives and staff
2. **Availability of equipment and drugs**
3. **Staffing**
   a. Number of staff (by professional profile) per population
   b. Age, sex.
   c. Training background.
   d. Activity descriptions.
4. **Organisation and management**
   a. Information management.
   b. Links with other levels of information exchange.

**Table 2. Process Indicators (adap. WHO, 1991a)**

1. **Accessibility** – Waiting list, opening hours.
2. **Initial assessment**
   a. How users are welcomed.
   b. Family members participation.
3. **Care process**
   a. How activities/time/staff are matched.
   b. Treatment process.
   c. Inter-staff relationship quality
   d. Relative's involvement in the treatment process.
4. **Discharge criteria**
   a. Information clearly spelt out.
5. **Patient information management**
   a. Confidentiality
   b. Patient access to own records
6. **After-care (follow-up, referral)**
   a. Patient/family informed how and where to continue treatment or to get social services
   b. Service to follow-up the patient receives adequate information on treatment received
7. **Legal rights**
   a. Clear information on nature/expected duration of treatment proposed
   b. To refuse treatment.
   c. To refuse admission
   d. Access his/her own record
   e. Access to own legal representative
   f. To appeal any decision.

*Process* can be defined as the set of diagnostic, therapeutic, preventive and rehabilitative procedures performed by a given service or department (table 2). In this respect it is possible to distinguish between two main components: the technical (concerned with expert skills) and the interpersonal (linked to the relationship between the health professionals and the patient/family members).

Process assessment has always been a normative, strictly professional activity that seeks to identify the degree to which the various procedures comply with pre-established standards and patterns.

Lastly, *outcomes* are the changes that the care provided brings about in the overall state of a patient's health, and frequently involve a difference between the objectives that were originally set and those that are actually achieved.

Outcome assessment is founded on the socially agreed value for each state of physical and mental health in terms of autonomy, integration, quality of life and so on (table 3). Contrary to process assessment, it should include the points of view of both the professionals (e.g. an evaluation of the degree of residual incapacity) and the patients (e.g. satisfaction with the care received) concerned.

**Table 3. Outcome Indicators (adap. WHO, 1991a)**

1. Classical indicators (e.g. mortality rate, length of stay, readmissions, discharge rate, turnover rate, bed occupancy rate)
2. Social integration
3. Disability level
4. Quality of life
5. Satisfaction with services
6. Side effects
7. Family burden

## Mental Health Care Evaluation: Problems and Obstacles

Given the constellation of people and elements that intervene in the process of providing care (patients, family members, specialist staff, the functional organisation of the health services, the nature of the therapeutic programmes, accessibility, etc.), assessing the quality of that care has proved to be a hugely complex task and has raised a significant number of questions.

From the conceptual point of view, besides the difficulties involved in defining the expressions *assessment* and *quality* themselves, the fundamental question lies in the legitimacy of applying the construct of quality, which was imported from the field of industrial and business management, to the healthcare context. In other words, we must ask ourselves to what point the omnipresent quality culture, which runs through so many aspects of our daily life, does not essentially reflect the tendency towards the hegemony of economic factors (i.e. cost reductions) in the way in which the health services are organised, to the detriment of those factors that are centred on the clinical and functional improvement of patients and their lives, or whether, on the contrary, its application represents some significant added value in the process of making health services suit patients' needs.

While it is also easy to come across conceptual problems of this kind in other fields of medicine, the singular context in which psychiatric and mental healthcare are provided raises a significant set of issues, including some of a methodological nature, which has been the object of intense controversy among the different researchers in this area (Caldas de Almeida, 1995; Brugha, 1996).

The first question that deserves particular attention involves the far-reaching changes that the structure, organisation and functioning of psychiatric services have undergone in the last thirty years. These can be illustrated by the progressive but irreversible replacement of the psychiatric hospital-centred model by the community model, in which provisions for outpatient and rehabilitative care are especially important.

The diversity of the care network is accompanied by the need for multidisciplinary teams that can encompass the whole range of patients' biological, psychological and social problems. This inevitably makes the levels of therapeutic intervention more complex and therefore more difficult to assess, given the *multiplicity of the variables* that must be controlled when indicators are analysed.

So when the effects of a given intervention or programme are assessed, how do we identify with a reasonable safety margin which agents and related procedures were directly responsible for the end outcome?

This problem becomes even more acute when we think that besides the aspects that are specifically linked to mental health services, there are many more that have a considerable influence on results. This is the case in questions related to primary healthcare (which plays a significant part in the care provided to people with psychiatric problems), the social services and the social support networks.

The second question basically concerns the *definition of quality criteria and standards* – something that presents additional difficulties in this field of medicine.

Given the lack of knowledge about the physiopathological mechanisms of mental diseases on the one hand and the existence of large differences between the theoretical models employed by healthcare professionals on the other, it is not easy to reach a consensus about what we conventionally call quality care. This makes establishing criteria and standards for the various different therapeutic interventions a very problematical task.

The thing is, just how do we define what is and what is not good quality care for each different psychiatric disorder?

While in some cases the nature of an intervention does make it possible to do so (e.g. the use of meta-analytical studies to establish criteria for the use of psychiatric drugs), when it comes to interventions of a psychosocial nature the definition of criteria and standards can only draw on expert opinions collected during bibliographic research – a method that almost always poses insuperable problems in relation to their validity.

Another important question is that of *defining the objectives* of the interventions and programmes that a service seeks to pursue and is related to the very nature of psychiatric disorders, particularly in the case of illnesses that take a long time to evolve.

It is not difficult to accept that without a set of properly identified and operationalised objectives, it is very difficult to assess the quality of the care that is provided in any psychiatric and mental health service.

In reality, however, it is precisely in the meaning of the term *care* that the problem of defining objectives is primarily centred.

In psychiatric disturbances the consequences of the pathological process go substantially beyond the expression of clinical symptoms and signs, and include the incapacities and disadvantages associated with both the illness itself and the way in which the person in question experiences it.

In direct correlation with this perspective, there have been discussions about the need to transform the thus far prevalent logic of *treatments*, which is derived from the traditional medical model, into a logic of *care*, which is a better match for the nature and extent of the problems that affect people with psychiatric disturbances (Wing, 1990).

This point of view, which implies a much broader approach to those problems than that on which the biomedical model (habitually restricted to the treatment aspect of the issue) is based, has raised additional difficulties when we come to define the objectives of psychiatric services. It is only more recently that these difficulties have begun to be overcome, thanks to conceptual and methodological developments in the need assessment field.

Finally, the last point concerns the influence of the factors that are used to select the procedural model that is to be employed – an aspect that is in turn closely related to the assessment culture that prevails in each different place, as we can see from the North American and European examples.

In the USA – a country in which health systems are organised and regulated in strict accordance with the laws of the market, in what some people call a prototype for the industrialisation of medicine (Baker, 1993) – assessments (mostly under the format of accreditation) are performed by bodies (e.g. JCAHO) that are not linked to the institutions which provide the care, and their outcome is mostly, albeit not exclusively, determined by whether or not budget figures have been met.

In Western European countries, where medical assistance is traditionally based on universalist-type national health services in which the separation between provider and financer is either not very clear or even non-existent, quality assessment is not only far less developed and widespread than in the USA, but is also usually carried out using internal auditing and self-monitoring methods in which the allocation of funding is not the central point of the procedure.

Above and beyond the specific characteristics derived from the different socio-economic models that we have just referred to, the major variations in terms of the procedural aspects of the assessment process inevitably raise some more questions about this topic: how effective really are assessment methods, and how should they themselves be assessed? What methodologically grounded scientific evidence is there for the advantages and disadvantages of each method? Which approach – external or internal assessment – leads *de facto* to a greater increase in the quality of the care that is provided, with the resulting benefits for patients, and not just to a simple reduction in costs? What impact does the participation of patients, family members and associations have on this process, particularly when looked at from the point of view of a comparison between the Northern and Southern European countries, where levels of empowerment are so different (Magliano, 1998; Magliano, 2000)?

The Rising of Outcome Indicators

The combined effect of the large number of variables in play, the difficulty of defining quality criteria and standards and the inadequate explanation of the objectives of therapeutic interventions has made the task of choosing the various indicators quite a difficult one, particularly when it comes to evaluating those forms of assistance that are structured in accordance with the community model.

The relative weight that ought to be attached to the various available indicators as measurements of quality continues to be a subject that is immersed in the deepest controversy (Micossi, 1993; Brugha, 1996). This greatly prejudices the drawing up of effective assessment programmes: in evaluating psychiatric care, what should be the role of the classic indicators (e.g. mortality, number of inpatient episodes, length of stay, etc.) and what are their main inadequacies, knowing as we do that the great majority of patients who suffer from serious psychiatric disturbances are not hospitalised (Jenkins, 1990)? Using Donabedian's (1980) classic definition, what is the benefit of information derived from structural, process and results indicators, and what are its limitations when we come to assess decentralised services?

For a long time, the difficulties experienced in the process of assessing the results achieved by mental health services (particularly in community models), and the limitations from which mortality and morbidity indicators suffer in the psychiatric context, meant that process indicators (e.g. number of appointments, number of hospitalisations) were used as indirect ways of measuring results.

However, as the data from clinical and epidemiological research built up, it became progressively clear that there was no direct correlation between the use of a given mental health service and the final result of its therapeutic interventions. As a result, beginning in the last decade there was a renewal of interest on the part of the scientific community in the use of outcome indicators.

The main question, which has been extremely controversial, then became: *which indicators should be used to assess outcomes?*

Modification of the psychopathological framework is undeniably an important indicator, but we have already seen that it cannot be used in an isolated fashion, because it does not reflect several of the aspects that are consensually seen as important to patient well-being.

Social functioning is another crucial outcome indicator. Initially seen as a simple epiphenomenon in the psychopathological framework, research has now shown that these two aspects are not necessarily correlated in transversal assessments (DeJong, 1986; Hecht, 1986) and can experience independent longitudinal evolution (Waryszak, 1982; DeJong, 1986).

What is more, social functioning appears to be dependent on the type of intervention that is being pursued. Amongst other things, when it comes to improvements in this respect the superiority of community models (especially integrated programmes) over hospital-centred ones has already been demonstrated (Olfson, 1990; Chamberlain, 1991; Test, 1992; Anderson, 1993; Audini, 1994; Burns, 1995; Marshall, 1995; Craig, 1997) – a fact that clearly reveals the indicators' discriminatory ability.

However, the great conceptual, methodological and operational advance that mental healthcare assessment has been experiencing in the last ten years is intimately related to the growing use of indicators which, although not specific to psychiatry, have enjoyed a notable degree of development in this field of medicine: *needs assessment*, *quality of life*, *satisfaction with the healthcare services* and *family burden*.

The justification for the great popularity of these instruments is twofold. In that the aspects in play are mixed – i.e. they possess both objective and subjective components – these indicators possess the enormous advantage that they are a perfect fit for the assumptions behind the WHO's concept of health, and permit an assessment of an eminently multidimensional kind.

In fact, if we accept that the assumptions made in the classic definition put forward by the WHO (1958) are valid, in addition to the clinical aspects, an assessment of the state of a person's health should cover the subjective side of an illness's impact. In this case, is it legitimate to limit the assessment of the result of a therapeutic intervention solely to factors of a clinical nature, or, on the contrary, should we obligatorily study another type of parameter, such as the patient's degree of autonomy, social functional level and quality of life?

This question is a particularly pertinent one in the context of psychiatric services, in which a very considerable proportion of the prevailing cases involves the treatment of serious chronic illnesses. Given that the prospect of total recovery is very often unrealistic, the development of psychosocial rehabilitation programmes has led to a whole panoply of changes in the way patients function, which it is only possible to evaluate using a multidimensional approach.

At the same time, their importance is also due to the disparities that exist between patients, family members and healthcare professionals when it comes to judging an intervention's value and impact, as can be seen from a whole range of studies (Sorensen, 1979; Morgan, 1989; McDonald, 1990; Ruggeri, 1993; Vicente, 1993; Biegel, 1995). If the points of view of the patient and his/her closest family members are not included in the assessment process, the isolated perception of the healthcare professional involved means that it is difficult for there not to be a degree of bias in the way in which the end result of any intervention is evaluated.

In this respect, it should be noted that the reservations that several authors (Sensky, 1992; Williams, 1995) have advanced in relation to the validity of the assessment by people with serious psychiatric disturbances of various aspects of the care that is provided to them (based on measurements with subjective characteristics) are in the process of being entirely refuted. On the contrary, the results of the most recent research reveal that such patients possess a considerable discriminatory capacity (Kelstrup, 1993; Svensson, 1994; Perreault, 1994; Ruggeri, 1996), including in inpatient settings – a fact that completely justifies their active participation in the assessment process.

The passage from normative assessment models – determined by healthcare professionals (or others) – to shared ones in which the opinions expressed by patients, family members and associations play a decisive role, is one of the most important steps in enhancing the empowerment of the users of mental health services.

However, reasons of a socio-cultural nature, among others, mean that this new philosophy has been implemented differently in the countries of Northern and Southern Europe. Assessment processes based on the opinions of patients and family members can make a very important contribution not only to improving the provision of care, but also to gradually altering the quality assessment culture itself, which has heretofore been limited in a strictly normative manner to professionals (healthcare and management).

We will now look at a study of this kind, which focuses on the assessment of care provided to patients with schizophrenia and the results of which provide an exemplary illustration of the importance of modifying our mental health quality assessment paradigms.

# AN EXAMPLE

## Context and Methodology

In 1991, after noting both the differences in the development of community facilities that existed between the various European countries and the shortage of reliable information about the different therapeutic models, the Planning Group on Mental Health Care in the European Community decided to promote a multicentric study that would permit an evaluation of the integrated care provided to people with severe mental illness (Freeman 1991).

Once this proposal had been made, a network known as ERGOS (European Research Group on Schizophrenia) was formed by ten university departments in seven European countries: France (Lille, Lyon, Saint Etienne and La Verrière, coordinator), Germany (Mannheim), Ireland (Dublin), the Netherlands (Groningen), Portugal (Lisbon), Italy (Cagliari) and Spain (Granada). Its objective was to assess the care needs of a population of schizophrenic patients and to determine the extent to which those needs were being met by an adequate response from healthcare services, thanks to a follow-up that was to be conducted one year after the study began.

The departments that were chosen to participate in the study all possessed a community philosophy linked to primary healthcare, but differed significantly in terms of the availability of structural resources (table 4), which can be summed up as a significantly smaller number of beds, day hospital places and sheltered residences in the Southern European centres, compared to those at the disposal of their Northern European counterparts.

This one-year prospective cohort study included 504 patients who had been clinically diagnosed as suffering from lifelong schizophrenia (ICD-10), as confirmed by SCAN – Schedules for Clinical Assessment in Neuropsychiatry (Wing, 1990), were aged between 18 and 65 years old and had had at least one contact with a mental health service during the year prior to inclusion.

From the point of view of the study group's socio-demographic characteristics, the "standard patient" was a single (77%) male (70%) adult (mean age – 38 years old) who had no children (86%) and was unemployed (88%). However, there were very significant differences in other variables, such as accommodation, with the great majority of patients in the Southern European and Irish centres living with their families, whereas in the Northern countries they lived alone, usually in apartments or sheltered residences, and in terms of the amount of support provided by the social services (e.g. pensions), which was much lower in the Portuguese and Italian centres.

No significant differences were found from the clinical point of view: the time of onset of psychosis varied between the ages of 18 and 26 years (average 22 years), while the first contact with mental healthcare occurred up to one year later, and nearly all patients were on neuroleptic medication.

**Table 4. Mental Health Facilities: Hospital Beds, Day-care Places and Sheltered Accommodation (per 1,000 of total population)**

| | Lille France 84,000 | Lyon France 118,000 | St Etienne France 206,000 | La Verrière France n.a. | Mannheim Germany 320,000 | Dublin Ireland 254,000 | Cagliari Italy 70,000 | Groningen Netherlands 998,000 | Lisbon Portugal 280,000 | Granada Spain 395,000 |
|---|---|---|---|---|---|---|---|---|---|---|
| Beds in general and psychiatric hospitals | .30 | .41 | .39 | n.a. | .90 | .38 | .21 | 2.29 | .10 | .14 |
| Places in day-care or day-hospitalization | 1.00 | .21 | .47 | n.a. | .04 | .59 | .00 | .74 | .04 | .06 |
| Places in sheltered accommodation | 2.60 | .14 | .13 | n.a. | .78 | .45 | .00 | .35 | .00 | .06 |
| Total of hospital beds, and places in day care/hospital and sheltered accommodation | 3.90 | .76 | .98 | n.a. | 1.72 | 1.42 | .21 | 3.38 | .14 | .26 |

**Table 5. Needs for Care Assessment Schedules (Brewin, 1997) – Clinical and Social Components**

| Clinical section | Social functioning section |
|---|---|
| Psychotics symptoms | Personal hygiene |
| Slowness/underactivity | Shopping |
| Side effects/dyskinesia | Get meals |
| Neurotic symptoms | Household chores |
| Dementia | Public transports |
| Physical symptoms | Public amenities |
| Dangerous behaviour | Education |
| Embarrassing behaviour | Occupation |
| Distress | Communication skills |
| Alcohol | Manage money |
| Drugs | Manage own affairs |

The evaluation of the need for care employed the "MRC – Needs for Care Assessment" tool (Brewin, 1987), which has been used in many studies (Thornicroft, 1996). This system characterises need status in three sequential steps: the first is to identify the patient's problems (*clinical* and *social functioning*, see table 5) by looking at a total of twenty issues (e.g. psychopathology, side effects of medication, hetero-aggressivity, the autonomous use of transport facilities, etc.) on the basis of data provided by the professional responsible for the case, family members and the patient him/herself. Despite other key-informants, the role of the family members was crucial for both problems and needs assessment.

The MRC-NCA specifies a group of potential therapeutic interventions for each of these areas of functioning. They are essentially rated in accordance with their effectiveness in terms of the resulting improvements in/recovery from the problems that had been identified. The combination of these two aspects (problem/appropriate intervention) defines the need status – an indicator that has been of great practical use in the systematised assessment of therapeutic interventions in the mental health field. The rating of both the level of functioning and the interventions can result in: no need (no problem), met need (problem is adequately taken care of), unmet need for assessment, unmet need for treatment (no effective and acceptable intervention is being delivered), and no meetable need (a potentially effective intervention is either not available, or is being refused by the patient).

## Main Results

In the first NCA assessment the *clinical* areas with the most problems were psychotic symptoms (87%), slowness and underactivity (58%), and dyskinesia or other side effects of medication (33%).

Like the pattern that was found for the different centres in relation to the whole of the population under study, this suggests that there is a set of clinical problems that is relatively independent of the nature and structure of the therapeutic setting (Brugha, 1988; Wiersma, 1996c).

When it came to the impact of the provision of care (table 6), the overall level of met needs (79%) and the similarity between the met/unmet need ratios for Northern and Southern Europe thus appear to show a similar degree of effectiveness in the various centres' responses to the needs in the clinical field. This result in fact matches those of various other preliminary studies that had been carried out in a number of European countries and Canada (Wiersma, 1996). Even so, the proportion of unmet needs returned by the Southern European centres was above the overall average, although the low percentage of non-meetable needs in some centres (e.g. Lisbon, Granada) could suggest that there are situations in which the non-resolution of a problem was due to the fact that the solution was never even proposed to the patient.

As far as *social functioning* is concerned, the largest number of problems was related to *occupational skills* (42%), *managing own affairs* (41%), *managing money* (35%) and *problems in carrying out household chores* (33%).

Curiously, and despite the general similarity between the various centres, there were significant differences in the *domestic tasks (basic, purchases, kitchen)*, in which the patients from the Southern European centres displayed far more problems than their counterparts in the North.

This clearly demonstrates the crucial importance of carrying out comparative studies of countries where the realities of life are different. The interpretation of results of this kind should obligatorily include aspects of a socio-cultural nature, failing which they may lead to unsuitable generalisations and extrapolations. In this case the nature of the roles that Southern European society allocates to males – already pointed out in earlier studies (Lesage, 1991) – meant that it was necessary to question whether the non-performance of basic domestic tasks was or was not a concrete problem that required intervention in those cases in which the patient's family regularly provided him with this type of care (Xavier, 1999).

Briefly, the point was whether or not we ought to consider that a patient living with relatively young parents who manage the affairs of the household really has a problem and therefore an unmet need? Or whether we should restrict the unmet need status to patients with older parents or an inadequate family network? Just how should the need status be rated in this situation?

In reality, if one were to follow the rules strictly, one might predict a lot of unmet needs in the home-life area, despite the fact that we know how cohesive families in the Southern European countries are in general, and that we are familiar with the lack of opportunities to display competence in these areas of functioning. Moreover, if we were to consider all these situations (or the majority) to be *non-applicable*, we would lose the instrument's discriminative power.

Although other studies (Lesage, 1991) have opted to consider such cases to be "non-applicable" for rating purposes, in this project we decided to proceed differently (albeit applying the same method to all the centres). We considered that a problem did exist whenever we detected a limitation on an acceptable level of autonomy, and emphasised the role that external agents (family, support network) played in determining need status, thereby avoiding excessively normative stances. Thus, a problem was always considered to be present if the patient was expected to live with an acceptable level of autonomy. If the family was acting in a way as a sheltered environment, and probably would continue to do so in the near future, the need would be rated as met. Other cases, where the patient was considered to be by himself in the short or medium term/for a short time on average (e.g. older parents, weak social network), were rated as *unmet need*. These procedures clearly ensured the distinction between different situations, and at the same time respected the cultural reality of the Southern countries.

When assessing need status in this section of the study, we found a very marked contrast with the results from the clinical section, which clearly reflected the lower degree of efficacy of the response that the various centres offered to patients' needs in the social functioning field.

However, contrary to what happened with the needs in the clinical section, when all the centres were compared with one another, the pattern of social functioning care need statuses was clearly bimodal: the Northern European countries (except for Ireland) returned a met/unmet need ratio that was above the overall average, whereas the southern centres returned much lower ratios. What is more, if the needs of many of the patients from the south of Europe had not been met by their families, the difference between the ratios would probably have been much greater still (Xavier, 2002).

This data was the critical result produced by the first phase of the project, inasmuch as it very clearly showed that when it came to clinical (based on medical care and most especially psychopharmacological interventions) effectiveness, the differences between centres were not very significant, whereas in terms of their effectiveness in the psychosocial area (which is dependent on the existence of structured rehabilitation programmes) the centres in the south of Europe, which were gifted with fewer community resources, yielded results that were substantially inferior to those of their northern counterparts.

The link between the number of unmet needs and the development of community structures was assessed statistically and revealed the existence of a highly significant negative correlation between unmet social needs and the number of places available in both day units ($r = -77$, $p = 0.01$) and community residences ($r = -82$, $p = 0.009$).

In contrast to unmet social needs, unmet clinical needs were not related to either the number of beds or that of community places: the correlation between the total number of beds and day or sheltered places in mental healthcare units and the number of unmet social needs is statistically highly significant ($r= -.90$; $p= .001$), but this is not the case with unmet clinical needs ($r= -.40$; $p= .29$).

However, this study also raises yet more questions that are no less important to the subject of the assessment of the quality of care: inasmuch as the majority of the differences between the centres were to be found in the social functioning area, how could this assessment's discriminative power be guaranteed if the problems had been identified in a solely normative manner? How could the corrective mechanisms that matched the needs expressed in the study be activated?

The significant improvement in need status that was found in both the clinical and the social areas in the follow-up assessment conducted a year later (table 7) is the best answer to these questions and clearly demonstrates the importance of patients' and family members' participation in the process of assessing mental health services.

Although in Southern Europe family participation in the process of assessing healthcare services is already increasing, the same cannot be said of the family's role in planning patient care. The truth is that therapeutic plans are still almost exclusively drawn up by specialist staff and are generally put to patients without involving their families.

## Table 6. Clinical and Social Areas – Problems, Need Status and Ratios

| | Lille N=46 | Lyon N=44 | St Etienne N=50 | la Verrière N=27 | **France** | Mannheim N=66 | Dublin N=54 | Groningen N=48 | **North Eur** | Cagliari N=19 | Lisbon N=50 | Granada N=81 | **South Eur** | Average N=419 |
|---|---|---|---|---|---|---|---|---|---|---|---|---|---|---|
| Perc. clinical met needs | 75.80 | 80.52 | 79,80 | 93,67 | | 80 | 75 | 56.88 | | 69.47 | 79.73 | 79.01 | | 76.96 |
| Perc. clinical unmet needs | 70.10 | 4.50 | 9.30 | 0,00 | | 11 | 5.60 | 15.60 | | 15.00 | 14.3 | 7.1 | | 8.60 |
| Perc. clinical no meetable needs | 13.08 | 13.14 | 9,43 | 2,20 | | 9 | 9.69 | 18.06 | | 9,82 | 2.37 | 6.70 | | 9.42 |
| Perc. social met needs | 67.47 | 68.94 | 75.14 | 66.20 | | 72 | 51.92 | 60.73 | | 35.97 | 67.03 | 41.34 | | 59.67 |
| Perc. social unmet needs | 25.76 | 17.77 | 34.68 | 0.90 | | 8 | 16.26 | 12.50 | | 41.57 | 29.08 | 48.59 | | 27.12 |
| Perc. social no meetable needs | 27.49 | 20.53 | 29.26 | 27.33 | | 20 | 26.54 | 24.81 | | 23.38 | 0.00 | 17.89 | | 21.61 |
| Ratio met/unmet clinical needs | 11.57 | 16.25 | 6.22 | | **11.67** | 7.3 : 1 | 17.33 | 4.21 | **8.15** | 4.3 | 5.2 | 12 | **7.27** | 8.88 |
| Ratio met/unmet social needs | 4.33 | 3.53 | 2.64 | 5.62 | **3.61** | 9.0 : 1 | 4.34 | 8 | **5.2** | 1.08 | 2.1 | 1.07 | **1.30** | 2.25 |
| Ratio met/unmet all needs | 6.36 | 6.52 | 4.22 | 16.12 | **6.16** | 7.8 : 1 | 7.03 | 5.47 | **6.38** | 1.86 | 3.13 | 2.47 | **2.56** | 3.98 |

## Table 7. Clinical and Social Needs – Status Evolution

| | Lille France | | Lyon France | | La Verrière France | | St Etienne France | | Mannheim Germany | | Dublin Irland | | Cagliari Italy | | Groningen Netherlands | | Lisbon Portugal | | Granada Spain | | Average | |
|---|---|---|---|---|---|---|---|---|---|---|---|---|---|---|---|---|---|---|---|---|---|---|
| | Inc | end | Inc | end | Inc | end | Inc | end | Inc | end | Inc | end | Inc | end | Inc | end | Inc | end | Inc | end | Inc | end |
| **Clinical Needs** | 2,4 | 2,1 | 3,8 | 3,3 | 3,4 | 2,9 | 3,7 | 3,1 | 3,5 | 3,9 | 2,1 | 1,8 | 3,5 | 2,2 | 2,1 | 1,52 | 3,5 | 3,1 | 3,4 | 3,1 | 3,1 | 2,6 |
| Met needs | 1,7 | 1,6 | 2,9 | 2,6 | 3,1 | 2,6 | 2,7 | 2,1 | 2,9 | 3,4 | 1,6 | 1,6 | 2,4 | 1,8 | 1,2 | 0,7 | 2,7 | 2,4 | 2,6 | 2,3 | 2,3 | 2 |
| Unmet needs | 0,1 | 0 | 0,1 | 0 | 0 | 0 | 0,4 | 0,3 | 0,4 | 0,2 | 0,1 | 0,1 | 0,5 | 0,2 | 0,2 | 0,3 | 0,5 | 0,3 | 0,2 | 0,3 | 0,2 | 0,2 |
| Not meetable needs | 0,3 | 0,4 | 0,5 | 0,4 | 0,1 | 0,1 | 0,5 | 0,5 | 0,3 | 0,3 | 0,2 | 0,1 | 0,4 | 0,1 | 0,4 | 0,2 | 0,1 | 0,2 | 0,2 | 0,2 | 0,3 | 0,2 |
| **Social Needs** | 2,6 | 2,6 | 3,1 | 2,1 | 2,5 | 2,5 | 2,2 | 2,1 | 2,6 | 2,8 | 2,6 | 2,5 | 4,7 | 3,3 | 1,8 | 1,6 | 3,1 | 2,5 | 3,5 | 3,8 | 2,8 | 2,6 |
| Met needs | 1,7 | 2 | 2,1 | 1,5 | 1,6 | 1,7 | 1,4 | 1,6 | 1,8 | 2,1 | 1,5 | 1,9 | 1,9 | 1,3 | 1,1 | 0,9 | 2 | 1,7 | 1,6 | 1,7 | 1,6 | 1,6 |
| Unmet needs | 0,3 | 0,1 | 0,5 | 0,1 | 0,3 | 0,1 | 0,5 | 0,3 | 0,2 | 0,3 | 0,3 | 0,1 | 1,7 | 1,2 | 0,1 | 0,2 | 1 | 0,6 | 1,5 | 1,1 | 0,7 | 0,5 |
| Not meetable needs | 0,8 | 0,5 | 0,6 | 0,5 | 0,6 | 0,7 | 0,7 | 0,4 | 0,3 | 0,5 | 0,5 | 0,2 | 1 | 0,7 | 0,4 | 0,5 | 0,1 | 0,1 | 0,7 | 1 | 0,6 | 0,5 |
| **Average Needs** | 5,0 | 4,7 | 6,9 | 5,4 | 5,9 | 5,4 | 5,9 | 5,2 | 6,1 | 6,7 | 4,7 | 4,3 | 8,2 | 5,5 | 3,9 | 3,1 | 6,6 | 5,6 | 6,9 | 6,9 | 5,9 | 5,2 |
| Met needs | 3,4 | 3,6 | 5,0 | 4,1 | 4,7 | 4,3 | 4,1 | 3,7 | 4,7 | 5,5 | 3,1 | 3,5 | 4,3 | 3,1 | 2,3 | 1,6 | 4,7 | 4,1 | 4,2 | 4,0 | 3,9 | 3,6 |
| Unmet needs | 0,4 | 0,1 | 0,6 | 0,1 | 0,3 | 0,1 | 0,9 | 0,6 | 0,6 | 0,5 | 0,4 | 0,2 | 2,2 | 1,4 | 0,3 | 0,5 | 1,5 | 0,9 | 1,7 | 1,4 | 0,9 | 0,7 |
| Not meetable needs | 1,1 | 0,9 | 1,1 | 0,9 | 0,7 | 0,8 | 1,2 | 0,9 | 0,6 | 0,8 | 0,7 | 0,3 | 1,4 | 0,8 | 0,8 | 0,7 | 0,2 | 0,3 | 0,9 | 1,2 | 0,9 | 0,7 |

Given that the family members are becoming such valuable resources as carers, it is crucial to assess their difficulties and needs, namely for the proposal of a psychoeducational intervention (Gonçalves Pereira, 1996; Xavier, 1999; Wijngaarden et al, 2000).

This is a very important point, as research has shown that informal carers (e.g. family members) of patients with severe and long-term mental illness may experience an important psychological and emotional burden.

A multicentric study (Italy, Portugal, UK, Greece and Germany) revealed that relatives of schizophrenic patients experienced higher levels of burden when they had poor coping resources (emotion-focused instead of problem-focused strategies) and reduced social support (Magliano, 1998, 2000).

In this study, emotion-focused strategies were more frequently found among those who had been living longer with the patient and who had poorer social support, as in Southern countries. Relatives in Mediterranean centres, who reported lower levels of social support, showed more resignation, and more often used spiritual help as a major coping strategy. In contrast, the adoption of problem-focused coping strategies was more frequent among young relatives and among relatives of younger patients, and was associated with higher levels of practical and emotional social support and of professional help, which would be much more available in Northern countries.

These results clearly revealed the impact of cultural factors in both family burden and coping strategies, raising the need to provide families with interventions focused on social network reinforcement and adoption of an effective coping style.

Furthermore, the results demonstrated the validity of family burden as an outcome indicator, reinforcing its importance in quality care evaluation.

## Final Remarks

For many years the changes that took place in the way psychiatric and mental health services were organised were largely stimulated and sustained by arguments of an ideological nature, and less often by facts revealed by hard evidence.

With the growing volume of results from the various lines of research that we have just looked at, scientific grounds began to replace ideology as the engine powering the transformation of the organisational structure of psychiatric and mental health services, at least in the industrialised western countries.

Quality evaluation is probably one of the most decisive of the factors included in that scientific grounding, quite apart from also being a counterpoint to the more money-oriented aspects of the way in which health structures are administered in general, and an element in the rectification of the asymmetries between the budgets of different psychiatric institutions in particular.

While we cannot expect that within the overall framework of governmental health priorities there will be an increase in the absolute value of the budget dedicated to implementing a new praxis of care, it is nonetheless clear that the structural and organisational transformation of conventional services depends first and foremost on the reallocation of existing resources.

Despite the sharp reduction in the number of long-term hospitalisations and the transition of the majority of patients into community programmes (which is where most new cases are also being followed) that have been occurring over the last few decades, the truth is that expenditure on psychiatric and mental healthcare is still being concentrated on psychiatric hospitals. At the beginning of the 1990's the latter consumed the lion's share of the overall budget for the psychiatric area, even in countries like the USA and the United Kingdom (80% and 70% respectively), where deinstitutionalisation has undeniably had a major impact on the transformation of the care systems (Raftery, 1992).

Under these circumstances, if the consistent, sustained development of a network of community care measures can only come about at the expense of the existing type of care, it is essential to carry out a rigorous assessment of the efficacy of the new system, compared to that of the previous one.

Thus, against the background of the profound transformations of the organisation of psychiatric and mental health services over the last four decades, it is no longer possible for those in charge of planning to issue any unilateral mental health policy directives without a scientifically based justification to document them, even given the possible (and inevitable?) methodological limitations to which that justification may be subject.

More than just a technical procedure, quality assessment must be seen as a guarantee of the fundamental rights of citizens in general and of patients with serious psychiatric disturbances in particular when they access and use health services.

From the large deinstitutionalisation projects to the small studies focused on specific therapeutic interventions, assessment is increasingly being seen as an essential element in integrating the technico-professional aspect of the issue with the value system that prevails in democratic societies, in such a way as to ensure that psychiatric and mental healthcare is provided on a fairer and more effective basis.

At the same time, assessing the quality of care in a scientifically rigorous manner could also be a powerful alternative to the growing hegemony that economic cost/benefit models have been attaining in the organisation of health services.

For this to happen, however, it is necessary to identify and overcome the obstacles that hinder the implementation of assessment procedures in the field, and to do so on three distinct levels: the operability of the methods employed; the resistance put up by professionals; and the real possibility for change to occur.

Moving onto the subject of *technical processes*, we know that due to its very nature, the specific field of psychiatry and mental health presents some additional operational difficulties: issues as diverse as the fact that there is no precise physiopathology for the great majority of psychiatric disturbances; the multiplicity of conceptual and technical guidelines; the difficulty of assessing certain therapeutic interventions (psychotherapies, psychosocial rehabilitation), and the impracticality of randomisation in many concrete situations. These are all unavoidable elements in this field of medicine and as yet we have no definitive solutions for them.

Research could play a fundamental part in this respect, thanks both to the development of the neurosciences (physiopathology) and to the use of quasi-experimental or observational-type studies, which more faithfully reproduce the conditions under which care is really provided.

The question of the connection between structural, process and results-based indicators in the psychiatric and mental health field has also been the object of significant developments in recent years. In this area the matrix model (Thornicroft & Tansella, 1999) naturally warrants particular mention. The use of two orthogonal dimensions – a temporal (structure, process and outcomes) aspect and a geographic (national, service, patient) one – permits a very comprehensive description of the various levels involved in the provision of mental healthcare.

Another critical challenge concerns the construction of simplified result assessment instruments that can be used in routine clinical practice – a task that has paradoxically been becoming more difficult due to the explosive growth in the number of ever more complex and differentiated, but also less ubiquitous, scales and questionnaires. Taking the ERGOS study we mentioned earlier as an example, it is perfectly apparent that the time needed to assess every case with the same battery of instruments would hardly be practicable in routine terms.

Managing to make care quality assessment a task that is an intrinsic part of a service's normal functioning requires the use of tools that possess specific characteristics, such as a bio-psychosocial approach to problems, simple and fast learning and use, applicability to a wide spectrum of clinical and social dysfunction situations, a good level of sensibility to change, a high degree of reliability, and compatibility with other instruments, the use of which has already been consolidated.

Solution of the methodological and operational problems alone is not, however, enough to ensure the successful functional implementation of a process of this kind within a department or service, because ultimately, that success depends on the actions of the health professionals in question.

As in any other system, we must always expect the appearance of active and passive *resistance* on the part of health professionals, many of which are legitimate. The scientific literature on the functioning and management of health services is full of examples in which in order to justify decisions that had already been taken unilaterally by administrative personnel, assessment was used to introduce changes that were radically opposed to staff expectations. There were also cases in which the procedures took so long that they could not be put into practice on a real-time basis, despite the fact that they had consumed a substantial amount of human and financial resources.

Implementing quality assessment in a health service thus requires a great deal of prudence and cannot be imposed on the professionals who provide the care: only an attitude of giving clear information that expressly includes the objectives and procedures that are to be pursued can make health professionals look upon this process as an integral part of their clinical practice.

By focusing the assessment process on patient needs rather than just the classic indicators (hospital rates and costs), we believe that the multidimensional assessment of the quality of care can make a considerable contribution to a reduction in the resistance put up by health professionals. For these people the word "assessment" continues to be more frequently associated with productivity problems (measured solely in terms of the number of acts performed) than with improvements in the provision of care.

In this phase, the participation of patients and family members is crucial, because it makes it possible to avoid excessively normative assessments and thus adapts the care that is provided to their own expectations and needs, which are often different from those presumed by the staff.

Lastly, it is necessary to ensure that whatever operational form the assessment may take, its results can lead to *concrete alterations in the structure and functioning of the healthcare services* in question, failing which the process may turn into an academic-style exercise and take away its primary purpose.

This is perhaps the most complex step in the implementation of quality assessment methods in the health field in general and psychiatry in particular, and can only be achieved by strengthening the *research*, *clinical practice* and *policy decision* triangle. This in turn implies conjugated contributions from various sides, such as health institutions, university centres, and the government bodies with responsibility for health on the one hand and patients, families and associations on the other.

Only by scientifically demonstrating the validity of the quality assessment procedures that are to be employed, first in studies with a restricted scope (at the individual level or that of therapeutic programmes) and then in studies that are widened to whole geographic sectors (at the level of a local health service and the way in which it is organised) are we likely to be able to intervene with solid arguments in the drawing up of mental health policies, thereby not only meeting patients' and family members' needs to the greatest possible extent, but also entirely fulfilling their rights as citizens.

## References

Anderson, J./Dayson, D./Wills, D./Gooch, C. (1993): The TAPS Project XIII – Clinical and Social Outcomes of Long-stay Satients after one Year in the Community; in: British *Journal of Psychiatry*, 162, 19, 45-46.

Audini, B./Marks, I./Lawrence, R./Connolly, J./Watts, V. (1994): Home-based versus out-patient/in-patient Care for People with Serious Mental Illness; in: *British Journal of Psychiatry*, 165, 204-210.

Bachrach, L. (1996): Deinstitutionalisation – Promises, Problems and Prospects; in: H. Knudsen, G. Thornicroft (eds.), *Mental Health Service Evaluation*, Cambridge: Cambridge University Press.

Baker, R. (1993): Avedis Donabedian – an Interview; in: *Quality in Health Care*, 2, 40-46.

Barton, W. (1959): *Institutional Neurosis*; Bristol: Wright.

Biegel, D./Song, L./Milligan, S. (1995): A Comparative Analysis of Family Caregivers' Perceived Relationship with Mental Health Professionals; in: *Psychiatric Services*, 46, 5, 477-482.

Brewin, C./Wing J./Mangen, S./Brugha, T. (1987): Principles and Practice of Measuring Needs in the Long-term Mentally Ill – the MRC Needs for Care Assessment; in: *Psychological Medicine*, 17, 971-981.

Brugha, T./Wing, J./Brewin, C./MacCarthy/Mangen S./Lesage A. (1988): The Problems of People in Long-Term Care – An Introduction to the Camberwell High Contact Survey; in: *Psychological Medicine*, 18, 443-456.

Brugha, T. (1996): Quality of Mental Health Service Care – The Forgotten Pathway from Process to Outcome; in: G. Thornicroft, M. Tansella (eds.), *Mental Health Outcome Measures*, Heidelberg: Springer-Verlag.

Burns, B./Santos, A. (1995): Assertive Community Treatment: an Update of Randomized Trials; in: *Psychiatric Services*, 46, 7, 669-675.

Burti, L. (1997): *Do we Still Need Mental Hospitals?* in: M. Tansella (ed.), Roma: Il Pensiero Scientifico.

Caldas De Almeida, J.M./Xavier, M. (1995): Avaliação e Garantia de Qualidade dos Serviços de Saúde Mental; in: *Acta Médica Portuguesa*, 8, 119-131.

Caldas De Almeida, J.M. (1996): Community Psychiatry in Portugal; in: *Epidemiologia e Psichiatria Sociale*, 5, 2, 92-95.

Chamberlain, R./Rapp, C. (1991): A decade of Case Management: a Methodological Review of Outcome Research; in: *Community Mental Health Journal*, 27, 3, 171-188.

Craig, T./Pathare, S. (1997): Assertive Community Treatment for the Several Mentally Ill in West Lambeth; in: *Advances in Psychiatric Treatment*, 3, 111-118.

DeJong, A./Giel, R./Soloff, C./Wiersma, D. (1986): Relationship between Symptomatology and Social Disability; in: *Social Psychiatry*, 21, 200-214.

Dickens, P. (1994): Components of Quality Health Care Services; in: P. Dickens (ed.), *Quality and Excellence in Human Services*, Chichester: Wiley.

Donabedian, A. (1980): The Definition of Quality: A Conceptual Exploration; in: A. Donabedian (ed.), *Explorations in Quality Assessment and Monitoring*, Ann Harbor, Health Administration Press.

Fauman, M. (1989): Quality Assurance Monitoring in Psychiatry; in: *American Journal of Psychiatry*, 146:1121-1130.

Freeman, H./Bennet, D. (1991): *Origins and Development;* in: D. Bennet, H. Freeman (eds.), Community Psychiatry, London: Churchill Livingstone.

Goffman, E. (1961): *Asylums – Essays on the Social Situation of Mental Patients and other Inmates;* New York: Anchor Books.

Goldberg, D. (1997): Community Psychiatry in Europe – Assessment and Evaluation; in: M. Tansella (ed.), *Making Rational Mental Health Services*, Roma: Il Pensiero Scientifico.

Gonçalves Pereira, M. (1996): *Repercussões da Doença Mental na Família – um estudo de familiares de doentes psicóticos*; MsC thesis, Lisboa: Faculdade de Ciências Médicas da UNL.

Häfner, H./Heiden W. (1996): Background and Roles of Evaluative Research in Community Psychiatry; in: H. Knudsen, G. Thornicroft (eds.), *Mental Health Service Evaluation*, Cambridge: Cambridge University Press.

Hecht, H./Wittchen, H. (1986): The Frequency of Social Dysfunction in a General Population Sample and in Patients with Mental Disorders; in: *Social Psychiatry and Psychiatric Epidemiology*, 23, 17-29.

Jenkins, R. (1990): Towards a System of Outcome Indicators for Mental Health, in: *British Journal of Psychiatry*, 157, 500-515.

Jenkins, R./Glover G. (1997): The Importance of Service Level Measures for Mental Health Policy; in: M. Tansella (ed.), *Making Rational Mental Health Services*, Roma: Il Pensiero Scientifico.

Kelstrup, A./Lund, K./Laurisen, B./Bech P. (1993): Satisfaction with Care Reported by Psychiatric Inpatients; in: *Acta Psychiatrica Scandinavica*, 87, 374-379.

Knapp, M. (1997): Economics and Mental Health: a Concise European History of Demand and Supply; in: M. Tansella (ed.), *Making Rational Mental Health Services*, Roma: Il Pensiero Scientifico.

Lesage, A./Mignolli, G./Tansella, M. (1991): Standardised Assessment of Needs for Care in a Cohort of Patients with Schizophrenic Psychoses; in: *Psychological Medicine*, 19, 27-34.

Lyons, J. (1997): Consumer Characteristics and Outcomes; in: J. Lyons, H. Kenneth (eds.), *The Measurement and Management of Clinical Outcomes in Mental Health*, Wiley, Nova Iorque.

Magliano, L./Fadden, G./Xavier, M./Maj, M. et al (1998): Social and Clinical Factors Influencing the Choice of Coping Strategies in Relatives of Patients with Schizophrenia – Results of the Biomed I Study; in: *Social Psychiatry and Psychiatric Epidemiology*, 33, 413-419.

Magliano, L./Fadden, G./Xavier, M./Maj, M. et al (2000): Family Burden and Coping Strategies in Schizophrenia – 1-year Follow-up Data from the Biomed I Study; in: *Social Psychiatry and Psychiatric Epidemiology*, 35, 109-115.

Marshall, M. (1995): Case Management: a Dubious Practice; in: *British Medical Journal*, 312, 523-524.

McDonald, L./Ochera, J./Leibowitz, J. (1990): Community Mental Health Services from the Users' Perspectives; in: *International Journal of Social Psychiatry*, 36, 3, 183-193.

Micossi, P. (1993): Measuring Products of Healthcare System; in: *The Lancet*, 341, 19, 1566-1567.

Morgan, S. (1989): Families' Experiences in Psychiatric Emergencies; in: *Hospital and Community Psychiatry*, 40, 1265-1269.

Olfson, M. (1990): Assertive Community Treatment – an Evaluation of the Experimental Evidence; in: *Hospital and Community Psychiatry*, 41, 6, 634-641.

Perreault, M./Rogers, W./Leichner, P./Sabourin, S. (1996): Patients' Requests and Satisfaction with Services in an Outpatient Psychiatric Setting; in: *Psychiatric Services*, 47, 3, 287-292.

Raftery, J. (1992): Mental Health Services in Transition: the United States and the United Kingdom; in: *British Journal of Psychiatry*, 161, 589-593.

Ruggeri, M./Dall'Agnola, R./Agostini, C. (1993): The Development and Use of the Verona Expectations for Care Scale (VECS) and the Verona Service Satisfaction Scale (VSSS) for Measuring Expectations and Satisfaction with Community-based Psychiatric Services in Patients, Relatives and Professionals; in: *Psychological Medicine*, 23, 511-523.

Ruggeri, M. (1996): Satisfaction with Psychiatric Services; in: G Thornicroft, M. Tansella (eds.), *Mental Health Outcome Measures*, Heidelberg: Springer.

Sartorius, N. (1997): Evaluating Mental Health Services – A World Perspective; in: M. Tansella (ed.), *Making Rational Mental Health Services*, Roma: Il Pensiero Scientifico.

Sensky, T./Catalan, J. (1992): Asking Patients about their Treatment – Why their Answers should not Always be Taken at Face Value; in: *British Medical Journal*, 305, 1109-1110.

Sorensen, J./Kantor, L./Margolis, R. (1979): The Extent, Nature and Utility of Evaluating Consumer Satisfaction in Community Mental Health Centres; in: *American Journal of Community Psychology*, 7, 329-337.

Svensson, B./Hansson, L. (1994): Patient Satisfaction with Inpatient Psychiatric Care – The Influence of Personality Traits, Diagnosis and Perceived Coercion; in: *Acta Psychiatrica Scandinavica*, 90, 379-384.

Tansella, M. (1997): The Key Role of Research in Making Rational Mental Health Services; in: M. Tansella (ed.), *Making Rational Mental Health Services*, Roma: Il Pensiero Scientifico.

Test, M. (1992): Training in Community Living; in: R. Lieberman R. (ed.), *Handbook of Psychiatric Rehabilitation*, McMillan, Nova Iorque.

Thornicroft, G./Phelan, M./Strathdee, G. (1996): Needs Assessment; in: H. Knudsen, G. Thornicroft (eds.), *Mental Health Service Evaluation*, Cambridge: Cambridge University Press.

Thornicroft, G./Tansella, M. (1999): *The Mental Health Matrix – A Manual to Improve Services;* Cambridge: Cambridge University Press.

Vicente, B./Vielma, M./Jenner, F./Mezzina, R./Lliapas I. (1993): User´s Satisfaction with Mental Health Services; in: International *Journal of Social Psychiatry*, 39, 2, 121-130.

Waryszak, Z. (1982): Symptomatology and Social Functioning of Psychiatric Patients before and after Hospitalization; in: *Social Psychiatry*, 17, 149-154.

World Health Organisation (1991a): Quality Assurance in Mental Health, Division of Mental Health; in: doc. *WHO/MNH/MND/90.11*.

World Health Organisation (2001): Burden of Mental and Behavioural Disorders; in: WHO (ed.) *The World Health Report*, Geneva: WHO, 19-46.

Wiersma, D./Giel, R./de Jong, A. et al. (1996): Assessment of Need for Care 15 years after Onset of a Dutch Cohort of Patients with Schizophrenia, and an International Comparison; in: *Social Psychiatry and Psychiatric Epidemiology*, 31, 114-121.

Williams, B./Wilkinson, G. (1995): Patient Satisfaction in Mental Health Care – Evaluating an Evaluative Method; in: *British Journal of Psychiatry*, 166, 559-562.

Wing, J./Brown, G. (1970): *Institutionalism and Schizophrenia;* Cambridge: Cambridge University Press.

Wing, J./Babor, T./Brugha, T./Burke, J. (1990): SCAN – Schedules for Clinical Assessment in Neuropsychiatry; in: *Archives of General Psychiatry*, 47, 589-593.

Wing, J. (1996): Evaluation and Public Policy; in: H. Knudsen, G. Thornicroft (eds.), Mental *Health Service Evaluation,* Cambridge: Cambridge University Press.

Winjgaarden, B./Schene, A./Koeter, M. et al (2000): Caregiving in Schizophrenia – Development, Internal Consistency and Reliability of the IEQ – European Version. Epsilon Study 4; in: *British Journal of Psychiatry*, 177, 39, 21-27.

Xavier, M. (1999): Quality Evaluation of Mental Health Services; *PhD dissertation*, Lisbon: Faculty of Medical Sciences.

Xavier, M./Caldas De Almeida, J.M./Martins, E. et al (2002): Needs for Care Assessment of Schizophrenic Patients in Portugal – Results from a Multicentric Study; *Revista Portuguesa de Saúde Pública*, 20, 2, 5-17.

# List of Contributors

**Brophy, Lisa:**
Chief Social Worker, North West Area Mental Health Service, Melbourne, Australia.

**Campbell, Jim:**
Senior Lecturer in the School of Social Work, Queens University Belfast, Northern Ireland.

**Bill Healy:**
Associate Professor in the School of Social Work and Social Policy, Latrobe University, Melbourne, Australia.

**Corbascio-Fox, Caterina:**
Psychiatrist; Psychiatric Rehabilitation Programme, Turin Mental Health Services; Lecturer, Department Psychology University of Turin, Italy.

**Crowe, Kieran:**
Director of Research Training & Policy, Irish Advocacy Network.

**Herrmann, Peter:**
Director of the independent Research Institute ESOSC – European Social Organisational Science Consultancy; Aghabullogue, Co. Cork. senior research fellow at the Department of Applied Social Studies University College Cork, Ireland.

**Irish Advocacy Network:**
A user run and user led organisation, providing information and support to fellow mental health service users, to empower them to speak up and take control of their own lives.

**Ramon, Shulamit:**
Professor of Interprofessional Health and Social Studies, School of Community Health and Social Studies, Anglia Polytechnic University, Cambridge, UK.

**Sapouna, Lydia:**
Lecturer, Department of Applied Social Studies University College Cork, Ireland.

**Taylor, Karen:**
Director of Advocacy, Irish Advocacy Network.

**Xavier, Miguel:**
Professor of Psychiatry, the Medical School, Lisbon New University, Portugal.

# INDEX

## A



## B

## C

## D



## E

## F



## G



## H

## I



## J

## N



## O



## P

## Q



## R

## S

## T



## U



## V